THE
SILVER ANSWER

In this fresh and thoroughly delightful biography, Constance Buel Burnett has re-created the story of Elizabeth Barrett Browning from her early girlhood in the home of her stern and possessive father, through her ecstatic courtship and subsequent marriage to Robert Browning, their inspiring life together in Italy and England, to the day of her death in Florence.

With beauty and sensitivity, the author has portrayed Elizabeth as a living, understandable human being, and has high lighted the facets of her life which motivated her writing.

Elizabeth Barrett Browing's poetry and letters will have new meaning to those who come to know Elizabeth through this sympathetic interpretation of her life.

"Guess now who holds thee?"—"Death," I said. But, there,

The silver answer rang—"Not Death, but Love."

SONNETS FROM THE PORTUGUESE

THE
SILVER
ANSWER

A ROMANTIC BIOGRAPHY OF

Elizabeth Barrett Browning

BY *Constance Buel Burnett*

DRAWINGS BY SUSAN FOSTER

NEW YORK *Alfred · A · Knopf*

THIS IS A BORZOI BOOK,
PUBLISHED BY ALFRED A. KNOPF, INC.

*This title was originally catalogued by
the Library of Congress as follows:*

92BRO Burnett, Constance Buel. The Silver answer. A romantic biography of Elizabeth Barrett Browning; drawings by Susan Foster.
1. Browning, Elizabeth Barrett, 1806–1861 2. Poets, English I. Title
Library of Congress Catalog Card Number: 55-6101 ISBN: 0-394-91623-9 (Lib. ed.)

❧ Acknowledgments

THE AUTHOR acknowledges her indebtedness to:
E. P. Dutton and Company, and John Murray (Publishers) Ltd., for permission to use excerpts from *Letters of Elizabeth Barrett Browning To Her Sister, 1846-1859,* edited by Leonard Huxley.

The Macmillan Company, and John Murray (Publishers) Ltd., for permission to use material from *The Letters of Elizabeth Barrett Browning,* edited by Frederic G. Kenyon.

John Murray (Publishers) Ltd., and United Feature Syndicate, for permission to quote briefly from *Twenty-Two Unpublished Letters of Elizabeth Barrett Browning and Robert Browning, Addressed to Henrietta and Arabella Moulton-Barrett,* and to quote extensively from the *Browning Love Letters.*

In addition, the author makes grateful acknowledgment to:

Jeannette Marks, for permission to use some of the material from *The Family of the Barrett* relating to the childhood and youth of Elizabeth Barrett and quoted in *The Family of the Barrett* from an unpublished Barrett Juvenilia in the Barrett-Browning Collection, owned by Jeannette Marks.

Elizabeth Reynolds Hapgood, for permission to use her translation of the epitaph to Mrs. Browning placed on the walls of Casa Guidi by the city of Florence.

The Wellesley College Library, for allowing the author to spend a day in the Browning Treasure Room.

THE
SILVER
ANSWER

❧ Chapter One

I called the place my wilderness,
For no one entered there but I.
THE DESERTED GARDEN

THE EAST WINDOW in the library had a deep,
wide sill. It was an ideal retreat for a person who
was only ten. Thick curtains made it a sanctuary from a
household teeming with adults and a growing flock of
younger brothers and sisters. Seated there, absorbed in
a volume of *The Tempest,* tilted against her up-drawn
knees, young Elizabeth Barrett was oblivious to the
rain drumming on the window pane at her elbow. She
heard only a beautiful cadence rising and falling from
the printed page.

The great house at Hope End, usually echoing with
the play of children and the footsteps of busy servants,
seemed muted by more than the weather today. Its master and mistress, Mr. and Mrs. Edward Moulton-Barrett

were away. That was why "Treppy," Grandmother Moulton-Barrett's Jamaican companion, was coming from Yorkshire to stay until their return.

Bro had gone to Ledbury in the chaise with James the coachman to meet Treppy's coach. Although a year younger than Elizabeth, he might have been her twin. At this early age the two looked much alike. Breadth of forehead gave promise of intellect. They had the same wide eyes which blazed darkly under stress of feeling, the same expressive mouth and the small chin that was a family trait.

From her window-nook in the library Elizabeth knew she would be the first to see Treppy's arrival, as the chaise wound along the tree-lined road of Hope End Park. Henrietta was still imprisoned in the schoolroom, droning her bored way through the multiplication table with Mrs. Orme, the governess. On rainy afternoons Sam, Arabel, and "Stormie," the baby, were banished to the nursery wing on the third floor, under Nurse's strict eye.

A leaf whipped by the wind suddenly hit the wet window pane where Elizabeth sat. Startled back to reality, she looked up from her book. Prospero, Ariel, and their island domain vanished. Through the soft English rain she saw instead the lawns of Hope End, spread like undulating velvet down to the pond's edge. Beyond the pond her mind's eye followed the brook, threading its way through the woods, meadows, and farms of her father's estate.

Elizabeth had come to Hope End too young to re-member any other home. She loved the immense house with its Byzantine dome and fortress-like towers and minarets. Not until much later would she be aware that it looked strangely out of key with the pastoral countryside of Herefordshire. Edward Barrett's wealth, acquired from sugar plantations in Jamaica, had allowed him to indulge a fancy for Moorish architecture.

In a tower facing the Malvern hills, he had planned a room for his oldest and favorite child, Elizabeth. Here a little girl, who was to feel the need of solitude early, drank in beauty with her native air and wrote numberless childish verses, imitative of the classics she was already greedily absorbing.

Interrupted now in her reading of *The Tempest*, Elizabeth let the book drop in her lap. Treppy would be here almost any minute. In fact, through the rain's tattoo on the window glass she already caught a sharper, quicker beat—that of horses' hoofs on the drive. At last the chaise with Bro and Treppy was approaching! Treppy—whose lightheartedness always injected a note of freedom into their lives!

She alone dared disregard the strict rules and regulations laid down by the "Monarch of Hope End" as his children nicknamed Papa. She was a privileged being at Hope End: a gay, ageless adopted aunt, who kept the children up beyond their bedtime for one more game or story oftener than Nurse or Mrs. Orme approved.

An hour later they were all gathered in Treppy's room to receive the presents she had brought. For Bro, who was clever at conundrums, there was a collection of *Choice Riddles* by Jeffrey Puzzlebrain.

"The answers are in the back—see, Bro," said Treppy

in her high, cheerful treble, so like a bird's chirping. Treppy was not much larger than a sparrow and just as intrepid and spry.

She wound up the next present and placed it on a table. "For Henrietta," she announced, pleased at the child's happy squeal over her music-box. Seven-year-old Henrietta was blessed with a pretty face, deep dimples, and "an ear for music," so Mamma claimed.

For Sam, who was six and very lively, there was a jumping-jack like himself. Arabel hugged her new doll, too shy to do more than look her thanks, and Stormie the baby was remembered with a rattle. Elizabeth waited in anxious silence.

"What is Ba going to get?" The question that was uppermost in both their minds burst from Bro.

"Never fear—I haven't forgotten her." Treppy laughed. "Her present happens to be at the bottom, that's all," and she drew a paper volume from her small horsehair trunk.

A book! Elizabeth flung her arms around Treppy.

"There—" Treppy beamed with pleasure. "I knew what our Poet Laureate of Hope End wanted above everything. Your grandmother picked it with great care. I know you will like it."

Elizabeth opened the book eagerly, but when she read the title eagerness vanished. *Blossoms of Morality: Intended for the Amusement and Instruction of Young Ladies and Gentlemen.* The books on the library shelves had beautiful names like *Paradise Lost,* and the novels by Amelia Opie which she devoured as soon as Mamma was through with them were so romantic they made you weep. She could have cried now with vexation! Bro saw that she could. He saw everything. But Treppy was watching too. Elizabeth made a great effort. "It sounds —most—most interesting, Treppy dear," she managed, at last.

By late afternoon the book had been dutifully read and tea-time brought the best part of Treppy's visit. For this was the hour when she carried them away to Jamaica, the far-away island in the Caribbean Sea which had once been her home, and where, before coming to England, Papa had lived till he was nine with Uncle Sam and Grandmother Moulton-Barrett.

She told them of the island's volcanic mountains, rearing jagged heads into the hot sky. She made them see the turquoise blue of the tropical water and how the nights in Jamaica were lit by stars as big as saucers. She made them hear the sighing of the trade winds in the palm trees.

Treppy remembered as far back as Great-Grandfather Barrett. He had ruled Cinnamon Hill Plantation and its hundreds of slaves like a potentate. She described the long black whip which used to hang in his plantation office.

"It was rarely used," Treppy said when she saw Elizabeth shudder, "your grandfather was considered a benevolent master. Flogging was only for those slaves who tried to run away."

"What made the slaves want to run away?" asked Elizabeth.

"They didn't try it a second time," Treppy assured her. "When your grandfather had to flog, he did it thoroughly."

"But you didn't say, Treppy, why the slaves ran away."

"La, child!" Treppy shrugged. "They didn't like being slaves, I suppose. A lot better off they were too, on the Barrett plantation, decently housed, clothed, and fed, than living savagely in their jungle."

Did Papa have to be punished for mischievous pranks —like other boys?—Bro wanted to know. But Treppy shook her head. "He was always a quiet lad. Your Uncle Sam now, was different. He would run off to the slave quarters. That was the naughtiest thing a child could do."

"Why?" demanded Elizabeth.

"Slaves were no fit companions for the Master's children."

"But Sam liked them," Elizabeth insisted. Uncle Sam, familiarly called plain "Sam," could do no wrong. "If I'd been there I'd have gone with him."

"Mercy on us—in my day little girls didn't think they knew better than their elders," replied Treppy tartly, somewhat nettled by the turn the conversation had taken.

She was thankful that Nurse appeared suddenly in the doorway. Further talk about slaves had to be postponed.

"We've caught nothing but minnows, Ba, aren't you going to fish any more? I promised Treppy we'd bring home a perch. But you tire so soon."

Bro wiped dirt-stained hands on his wide pantaloons. From the floor of the wooden bridge which spanned the brook he looked down with mild disapproval on his sister. Her own pantalettes were splashed with mud, her pink dress had a rent in the back. She lay flat on her stomach on a rock in mid-stream and watched the dark current turn to silver as it flowed through her fingers.

"I'm not tired—just thinking," she answered lazily.

Bro sighed. Elizabeth was like that. You couldn't count on her for long when it came to fishing. Sooner or later she wandered off by herself, up the hidden, twisting paths her thoughts took. Her fishing line lay forgotten beside her on the rock. Probably the bait he'd put on was gone too.

Havannah, the big black poodle, stretched beside Bro on the sun-baked boards, was more inert even than Elizabeth. Twice he had been slapped for upsetting the pail of bait, and, when he sniffed the wriggling minnows Bro pulled out of the stream, the hook had scratched him. Like Elizabeth he had retired from boredom up paths of sleep where he chased the quarries of his dream. His paws twitched. Once or twice he let out a muffled bark.

Elizabeth sat up suddenly. "I've thought a poem— want to hear the beginning?"

Bro's answer was a fierce whisper. "Hush up, do— I've got a nibble!"

Elizabeth edged quietly off her rock. Bro had eyes only for his taut line. She would slip away before she could see him take the struggling thing off the hook. Bro insisted that fish couldn't feel, but just the same, she thought, they must love to live in the sun-dappled water, to sleep in the shadows of overhanging ferns, and glide with the moving current. She knew, for she had been lying with her face very near that transparent world. She had seen how the minnow she had released from her cupped hands darted swiftly back to freedom. She had begun a poem about it.

The first line was "Oh, gentle minnow," but now, because Bro showed no interest, the rest was gone out of her head. It was no matter. She knew plenty of poems by heart. Reciting verse was even easier than making it up, and just as much fun.

"Piping down the valleys wild," Elizabeth murmured in time to her steps. That was out of a small volume called *Songs of Innocence*. It had been given her by an elderly neighbor, Sir Uvedale Price. She had heard people describe him with respect as "a man of letters." But Elizabeth was not in awe of him. His penetrating blue eyes always softened to a twinkle when he spoke to her.

Elizabeth had walked some distance from the woods and the stream where she had left Bro. In front of her, above the top of the sloping field, rose the turreted walls of Hope End House. Standing shoulder-deep in tall grass, enclosed in a green world where nothing stirred but the summer wind, she knew herself hidden from people in the house.

It seemed to her that even in her window seat in the library she had never been folded into stillness this way. The fields slept. A butterfly floated by. The birds were hushed and the insect creatures were drugged in the noonday sun. The hot air seemed heavy—weighted with a secret. If she stood very quiet she might hear it. She raised her face to listen—and then Bro hallooed.

"Ba—where are you!"

He was a great way off, but coming closer. His calls were splintering her beautiful silence. She must save it quickly! Running blindly, she pushed into a near-by thicket.

Bro went by without seeing. Even Havannah did not search her out, his nose being occupied with the fish that dangled near his muzzle from a stick. Watching them go, Elizabeth drew a deep breath and looked around her. She had stumbled into an old, neglected garden, screened from the lawns of Hope End by rank growth and untrimmed shrubs. Moss had encroached on its nearly obliterated paths. Four ancient rose trees formed a square. Their white blossoms shed a waxen gleam in the deep shade.

Enchanted by her discovery, Elizabeth sank down on the soft leaf mold. On that circle of moss under the old poplar, fairies must dance every moonlit night. Perhaps lovers had plighted their troth here long ago. This abandoned spot with its lost memories and secrets was all her own. She would tell no one of it—save Bro.

⊷§ Chapter Two

At four I first mounted Pegasus.
GLIMPSES INTO MY OWN LIFE
AND LITERARY CHARACTER BY E.B.B.

LORD MAKE ME to know the measure of my days on earth, to consider my frailty, that I must perish—" Edward Barrett intoned cheerless passages from the Scriptures as though he had a special relish for them.

To Elizabeth, Papa was never more the "Monarch of Hope End" than at this early hour in the morning when he read aloud from the Bible to the assembled household. As he stood in front of the long mullioned window in the Great Hall, a shaft of light illumined his portly figure. It shone on his carefully groomed hair and on the immaculate white stock under his plump chin. It seemed to invest him with deific approval.

Papa's prayers were as dramatic as his Scriptural readings. They had a dismal fervor which sent little shivers down Elizabeth's spine. She felt the same comfortable excitement from listening to the wind howl on a stormy night.

Sometimes the morning hour of devotion grew uncomfortably personal, as when Papa prayed over the failings and misconduct of his children; Bro's absent-mindedness, the pranks and tantrums of Sam and Stormie, Henrietta's inclination to be flighty, Arabel's habit of biting her nails, and Elizabeth's obstinacy. Recently, Papa had prayed evenings beside Elizabeth's bed so that she might understand the enormity of her rudeness the other morning.

She had met him on the stairs and smiled a good-morning without speaking.

"What—" Papa stopped her. "Not a word to me?"

"I have nothing to say," replied Elizabeth, in sudden revolt against the parrot-like "How are you Papa?" she said every morning.

"Will you not ask me if I am well?" Mr. Barrett persisted.

His query was sharp and the little girl hesitated. "No," she decided, "you would have told me if you had been ill."

Edward Barrett could scarcely believe his ears. Elizabeth—until this moment dutiful—the object of his intense pride, pitting her will against his! During the few seconds it took to lead her to the breakfast-room, Elizabeth remained defiant. Grown-ups, she kept telling herself, were hypocrites, always insisting on polite falsehoods. They wanted you to express concern for their health when nothing was the matter with them. Now Papa expected her to say she was sorry. Well—she wouldn't!

But just then Papa ushered her into the presence of the family and everyone around the table stared at her flushed face.

"This little girl," Papa announced in a voice icy with annoyance, "thinks it too much trouble to ask her father how he is."

In the silence which fell, Papa's displeasure had time to chill her as he intended it should. Secure in her knowledge of his love and approval, she had amused herself occasionally, imagining how it might feel to be cast out and abandoned, like the orphans in novels. Looking now at the frozen mask Papa wore, she knew with a shock how it felt.

Bro's spoon remained suspended half-way to his mouth. Was Ba going to be banished from her place as favorite? If so, he would go into exile with her. Henrietta, Sam, and Arabel were transfixed with admiration. Ba was very daring!

The cup Mrs. Barrett was holding under the tea-spout slid into its saucer with a nervous clatter. Lines of strain deepened in her patient face. "Oh, Ba, dear," she implored gently, then fell silent under her husband's look that said plainly: "Let me handle this, if you please."

Elizabeth hung her head. She had forgotten all about Mamma! How many times she had been cautioned too, these days, not to upset Mamma. It seemed terribly important all at once to undo what she had done. To comfort Mamma and be loved again by Papa.

"I'm sorry," she capitulated in a stifled voice.

Mamma relaxed visibly and went on pouring tea. Dennis entered with a plate of hot toast. He spoke deferentially to Papa. "Mr. Higgins is here to see you, sir."

"It's about Bradshaw, the new tenant, Ned." Mrs. Barrett welcomed the interruption eagerly. As she had hoped, Papa's concern for business closed the incident with Elizabeth—until bedtime, and evening prayers.

It had been a game for so long to pretend that Papa was a potentate, that no one could remember how it began. It was he, not Mamma who always decided everything—even the smallest matters.

"Ask Papa, he knows best," was Mamma's invariable answer to their requests. They accepted it without question, bestowing on the parent whose word was law the playful title of "Monarch." And how benign a monarch! Were not all their pleasures provided by Papa? Ponies to ride, pets, acres to roam, a pond for boating, streams to fish in?

"I believe you have anticipated the children's every wish, Edward," Elizabeth once overheard Grandmother Moulton-Barrett tell Papa.

"If I have erred, it is in being too indulgent," was his gratified answer.

Behind the library curtains, Elizabeth caught a great deal she was not intended to hear. It was not her fault. She had not hidden there on purpose. Absorbed as she was in her books, much of it passed over her head. But she heard enough to be conscious of smothered conflict underneath the adult conversation at Hope End.

Concealed in her favorite refuge one day, she was

startled to hear Papa name the title of the book in her hands.

"There is a volume of Goethe's missing from the third shelf, Mary, my dear—*The Sorrows of Werther*. Where is it gone?"

"I fancy Elizabeth may be reading it, Ned. I will look in her room."

The click of scissors and thimble being laid on a table meant that Mamma was preparing to rise. Papa must have stopped her with the gesture of the lifted hand Elizabeth knew so well, since he said immediately:

"That is hardly possible, Mary. I gave her no permission to do so."

"But *I* did, Ned. There can be no harm in Goethe, surely. Ba is always wanting something to read. She has outgrown children's books. You are not displeased?"

Elizabeth knew Mamma's hands were fluttering now, performing the motions of sewing in a trembling, bewildered way. She knew too, without being able to see, that Papa's mouth was drawn into a tight line. Elizabeth held her breath in the silence.

Papa cleared his throat.

"I thought, my dear, you understood my wish to be consulted in all matters concerning the children. I am grieved, yes—but not displeased. Grieved that you should have forgotten."

"Indeed, Ned, I didn't forget—but you were in London for several days and the matter seemed urgent to the child. I'm sorry it happened," the soft voice faltered.

"It is my earnest wish," Papa repeated, "that the children may never be deprived, as I was, of a father's wise counsel and devotion."

Elizabeth knew very little about Papa's father, Charles Moulton, except that Grandmother had never seen him again after she left Jamaica for England. She had been told too, that Papa had changed the family name from Moulton to Moulton-Barrett when he came of age and inherited the Barrett plantations.

After that brief talk between Mamma and Papa, Elizabeth needed no prompting. Later in the day she approached her father. She was already learning how to dissipate gathering thunderclouds.

"Puppy, dear—" it was her special name for him—"I found *The Sorrows of Werther* on the shelf here and couldn't wait to ask your permission to take it out. Say you forgive me!" She hung affectionately on his hand, and Edward Barrett was softened.

"I'm pleased to have you read the great authors. However, at your age, you can be no judge of what is proper. Don't read Gibbon's *History,* or *Tom Jones,* or any of the books on this side—mind!"

"Yes, Papa." Elizabeth nodded obediently. How fortunate that on the other side of the library were any number of books not explicitly forbidden by Papa!

Papa made everything much easier by stating his wishes precisely and insisting on being obeyed to the letter. So Elizabeth read Tom Paine, Voltaire, Hume, Rousseau, and Mary Wollstonecraft, none of whom he had mentioned, and all of whom fed her hungry young mind with dangerously new and exhilarating ideas. But the Greek books in the library at Hope End were a closed world to the little girl, being written in letters she could not decipher. She had implored Papa for permission to learn Greek, and now her heart's desire was about to be granted, due, in part, to a remark dropped by Sir Uvedale.

Sir Uvedale Price, eminent scholar and a man of varied gifts, received Mr. Barrett cordially whenever he called on him at Foxely Hall, in Herefordshire, not far from Hope End. A neighborly relationship had sprung up between him and the rich West Indian planter who sometimes sought his advice on the education of his boys.

Mr. Barrett's manners betrayed self-importance, to be sure, and his talk, to a man of Sir Uvedale's mellow temper, seemed opinionated, but this was understandable. Jamaican planters lived like potentates on their holdings. The autocratic tradition was too strong to be erased by a few years in England. Under the circumstances it was the more to Mr. Barrett's credit that he had ambitions for his eldest daughter, Elizabeth. Most fathers of Sir Uvedale's acquaintance thought their girls hardly worth the expense of educating.

"I've always thought it a pity women aren't given the same opportunities as men to develop their minds," Sir Uvedale had remarked one day. "Your daughter Elizabeth, for example, Mr. Barrett, is brilliant, she could probably go far in scholarship."

Mr. Barrett had been gratified and had reconsidered Elizabeth's plea.

"You sweetest, dearest, kindest Puppy—you will see

how hard I shall study," Elizabeth promised when her wish was granted. She loved Papa and thanked him in grateful superlatives. For, after all, what desires had she ever had that Papa, the benevolent despot at Hope End, had not granted—when propitiated and pleased?

The tutor engaged to teach Greek at Hope End was surprised to find the girl the more gifted of his two pupils. Elizabeth worked with passionate eagerness and a fury of concentration. Reciting and writing with maddening accuracy, she drove Bro to an equal effort if not equal enthusiasm. They were a matched pair, but it was she who set the pace.

Grandmother Moulton-Barrett was the only member of the family who questioned the desirability of so much learning for a young female.

"Where will it all lead to?" she asked. "I would rather see Elizabeth's hemming more carefully finished off than hear all this Greek. Greek, after all—" she turned to her daughter-in-law for support—"is no preparation for marriage."

"Marriage!" exclaimed Edward Barrett. "Dear Mother, the possibility is too remote for consideration!"

"You forget—Elizabeth will be sixteen in four years. Besides, you, yourself," Mrs. Moulton-Barrett reminded her son with some asperity, "insisted upon marrying at nineteen.

"Of course," she pursued a topic which to her was all engrossing, "the marriage portions you will be able to settle on your girls should vastly help their prospects."

"Are you suggesting," her son asked, after an astounded pause, "that I encourage fortune-seekers?"

"Surely you must expect, Edward—"

But the master of Hope End was no longer listening. He had risen from his chair. Aware suddenly that she was addressing his uncommunicative back, Mrs. Moulton-Barrett stopped.

Before quitting the room, Edward Barrett turned for the ceremonious good-night he never omitted. "You will excuse me, my dear Mother. Dispatches from Jamaica must be answered."

"There Bro, that's all!" Elizabeth announced triumphantly, as she came to the end of the long poem she had been reading. Written in clear, careful penmanship, its thirty or so pages lay in her lap.

The recent Greek lessons and her enchanted perusal of the *Iliad* and the *Odyssey* had inspired Elizabeth to write a poetic saga of her own. Her theme was the battle of Marathon. She had worked on it all this summer vacation, spent (because of Mamma's health), at Ramsgate on the sea.

While Bro knelt beside her on the beach, his hands idly shaping a sand fort, Elizabeth waited with caught breath for the climax of praise she hoped—she was sure —was to be her reward!

"It's wonderful, Ba," Bro obliged almost immediately, "really wonderful! We've been here only five weeks— and you've written enough for a book!" He sat back on his heels, the better to marvel.

"Oh, well—it was easy. Words kept pouring out!" Elizabeth tried to sound modest, but she was bursting with elation as she folded her masterpiece and stuffed it back into her pinafore pocket.

How golden lay the yellow sands along the curved shore, how dazzlingly clear shone the distances, seen through her triumph! Far up the beach, Mamma's red cotton umbrella sang a jubilant note against the blue water. Beside the weathered gray of the bathing machine—the bath-house on wheels which Papa had rented for the season, Nurse's starched apron gleamed whitely, and the dresses of little George and Henry. Near them, four bare-legged children in striped jerseys brandished long-handled nets as they waded in the low tide, calling shrilly to each other. Sam, Stormie, Henrietta, and Arabel were crabbing industriously.

It was understood by younger brothers and sisters that Elizabeth and Bro went off on their own Olympian pursuits and were not to be bothered. Every afternoon the Poet read to her audience of one what she had composed during the morning. Each day his applause strengthened her modest conviction that "The Battle of Marathon" was a remarkable poem. With such encouragement "words kept pouring out" in a simply intoxicating stream!

It was wonderful, too, that the completion of her epic coincided exactly with the end of their seaside vacation. On the long ride home from Kent to Herefordshire everyone else grew bored, but Elizabeth hugged to herself the knowledge that she would soon be famous. She could hardly wait to see how much better her poem was than Pope's Homer in the library.

She smiled when she remembered all the silly rhymes she had once written. In those days Papa had dubbed her "Poet Laureate of Hope End." Today—how prophetic his little joke!

The towers of Hope End rose at last on the horizon. The long, winding trip through the park commenced. Now she and the other children were running through the wide-open front door, framed by Dennis and the curtsying staff of maids. In the confusion and uproar of greetings and getting settled, it was easy to snatch Mr. Pope's version from its shelf and rush with it to her room.

For the first time since leaving Ramsgate, Elizabeth re-read "The Battle of Marathon" by Elizabeth Barrett. She found its excellence unimpaired by the lapse of time. Then, eagerly and much too confidently, she opened Pope's Homer. The descent from vainglory was swift.

Her first impulse to tear "The Battle of Marathon" to bits gave way to reason. Line by line she decided to compare her verses with those of Mr. Pope, to learn, if possible, why and how she had failed. The dream of fame seemed so distant now as to be out of sight. Its ladder was too steep for such as she. But she could follow worshipfully many rungs below those who were at the top—and she would never abandon the climb.

With all its clichés and hollow apostrophes, "The Battle of Marathon" was an impressive feat for a thirteen-year-old poet. Edward Barrett thought the time devoted to Greek lessons well spent. He ordered fifty copies of the poem printed, and proudly distributed them among relatives and friends. Its author was not elated when she saw her work in print, but she thanked Papa properly. He had meant to please her. She understood the praise of adults now. It was not for the poem, but for a little girl who had written the best she knew how. The lesson administered by Mr. Pope was never forgotten.

☙ Chapter Three

Scarcely I was a woman when I lost my
mother . . . .
LETTERS OF ROBERT BROWNING
AND ELIZABETH BARRETT

ELIZABETH leaned confidingly against her uncle
as the carriage which was bringing them both
back to Hope End swung off the highway onto the
Ledbury road. Uncle Sam, Papa's younger brother, did
not resemble Papa in the least. He had no commanding
presence, no Jovian displeasure. He was boyish and gay.
His disposition, in fact, was altogether too easy—so
Papa said. But then, Papa was a ruler—and Sam just an
uncle.

The new green bonnet lying in Elizabeth's lap had
been Uncle Sam's contribution to her holiday in London.
It had a becoming poke brim and a small, soft ostrich

plume. He tied it under her chin with a flourish before leading her to the looking-glass.

"Let me present Miss Barrett—late of the schoolroom at Hope End, and now—" Sam Barrett left the sentence unfinished. Meeting her delighted gaze in the mirror, he made her a flattering bow. His choice of bonnets had been a happy one. The note of fashion above the wide brow and serious eyes gave Elizabeth an unaccustomed and bewitching elegance.

It had taken all her cajolery to win her father's consent for this week in London. The trip had been Uncle Sam's idea. He had wanted to soften the shock of Bro's departure for Charterhouse School. Close companionship with her favorite brother was at an end. Sam Barrett had even supposed her father would agree with him, that, now she was fifteen, Elizabeth should begin to see something of the world.

"Let her come to Mother and me at Carlton House for the winter," was his first proposal, "there is a pleasant group of young people in the neighborhood. I dare say it would do Elizabeth a world of good to get away from books right now."

"Elizabeth prefers books to frivolous amusements and associates," objected Edward Barrett.

"That's because she's had no friends her own age," Sam retorted, "no companions at all except younger brothers and sisters."

"You entirely mistake her needs, I think," her father answered, and with such finality the subject had to be dropped. Defeated, Sam turned on his heel, but not before he delivered a telling shot. "You don't love Elizabeth as much as I do," he remarked quietly. "You see only your need to keep her by you."

As their coach bowled along the familiar country lanes, Elizabeth hardly knew whether to be glad or sorry her London visit was over. It was going to be such fun to describe all she had seen and done to an attentive home audience—the London shops, the fashionable equipages, Vauxhall gardens, the changing of the Horse Guards. She could picture the round-eyed astonishment of the less traveled Henrietta and Arabel!

Then too, she was re-entering the peaceful charm of Herefordshire. By contrast, the cries of street-hawkers, the bustle, clamor, and stimulation of a great city, were remembered as a big confusion. Secretly, almost guiltily, she hugged the thought of return to books. They were her dearest companions, except for Bro— without him, her greatest solace.

Sam Barrett rode beside his niece in troubled silence. Of his brother's children, she was the most deeply loved. "Will she see the need of escape?" he asked himself. "Hope End with its loved inmates is too pleasant a jail and she has a fierce loyalty to its keeper."

"You're almost grown, Ba." He spoke on a sudden impulse, because so intimate a moment together might not recur. "You will want to marry some day—and I may not be here then."

"Not here?" Elizabeth's eyes widened with apprehension. "Oh, Sam—where are you going?"

"Sooner or later some of us Barretts must live in Jamaica—to look after family interests there."

Jamaica! The island she had never seen loomed in the background of all their lives and controlled their destinies. A source of great family revenue, it was also the cause of periodic family separation and pain.

"Beware of loving, when the time comes," she heard Sam Barrett say, "you don't do things by halves, Ba." He lightened his advice with a smile. "When you love, it is for life and death."

Much later she was to remember the warning. At the moment nothing mattered but the fact that he might leave England. "We'll come and visit you in Jamaica—Bro and I," she assured him. He saw the idea comforted her and did not remind her that Edward Barrett would forbid it.

Despite the rich resources of the Hope End library, Elizabeth knew moments of acute loneliness now her brother was away. There was no one left to share a young poet's swift changes of mood and harebrained impulses.

One autumn day, looking wistfully out at a sky full of whirling leaves, she remembered how often in November she and Bro had ridden their ponies full tilt before the wind, giving them their heads, exulting in the headlong race across the fields.

Who was there to go with her now? Certainly not Henrietta, still playing with dolls and liking best to drive tamely in the barouche with Mamma. Not young Sam, named for his uncle and now away at school. Nor by the widest stretch of the imagination, Arabel, gentle since the day she was born, and disliking boisterous games.

Oh, for a hard gallop to free body and spirit! Elizabeth ran out of her room, swept by a passionate need for release.

The stable, when she reached it, was empty. She remembered then that the horses were all gone to Ledbury to be shod. Not even a stable boy was left on the place.

"I'll saddle Moses myself," Elizabeth decided.

Moses, her black pony, trotted up eagerly when she opened the gate of his pasture. "We'll have a frolic," his owner promised him as he nuzzled her pocket for sugar. It took but a minute to slip the bridle on. Hoisting the heavy saddle, however, was more difficult than she expected, and Moses grew restless because the hands fumbling at his girth were inexpert and slower than usual.

Finally the cinch held—or so Elizabeth thought. She had raised herself in the stirrup, in the act of mounting, when the buckle pin slid and the saddle fell off, carrying her with it.

Something was wrong, Moses knew. He had sense enough to stand still until she was on her feet again, but his rider had wrenched her back badly. There was no one within calling distance, so she managed to put the pony back in his pasture and limp home, although each step seemed an agony.

Before the injury to her back was healed, Elizabeth was stricken with pneumonia. For a few days her life was in danger. Afterwards, it was pleasant to recover slowly by the fire in the library, surrounded by all the books she wanted, and waited on by two adoring sisters.

It was Elizabeth who dominated Hope End when Papa was not there. From the beginning her initiative and imagination had invented games and led them in play. But she and Bro had soon outgrown the nursery and schoolroom, outstripping the others and unconsciously shutting them out of an intimate private world for two. Often since his departure for Charterhouse, Elizabeth reverted to the habit of slipping away from the family circle. Heedless of everything but her need to get away by herself, she would run to her secret hiding place in the abandoned garden she had found, to read and dream there alone.

Now, in weakness, the companionship of the others was suddenly comforting. She was glad to be one of them, content just to sit, listening idly to the cheerful chatter around her. No longer so engrossed in herself, she began to notice things she had been blind to before.

What a loving nature Arabel had—and, alas, what a plain little face! But when the sun touched her hair it was changed to spun gold, and her smile was very sweet. Henrietta's laugh was contagious and her complexion like strawberries and cream. They were both sweet-tempered and good and much more unselfish than she, thought Elizabeth, remembering guiltily that she ran off too frequently to a world of books in which they had no share. Well—she could make it up to them, right now!

"The hours do fly, Ba, when we're with you," exclaimed Arabel happily, adding with great care a curled stem to the ivy she was tracing on a china saucer. While she painted and Henrietta sewed, Elizabeth read aloud from a novel borrowed from Mamma.

Stormie, George, and Henry, the despair of their Latin tutor, brought the Gallic wars to the library because the old Romans came wonderfully to life when Ba could be persuaded to lend a hand at translating. Even Mamma, usually busy upstairs, heard the lively talk there and came too, carrying sketching materials she had not touched for years. She drew a pencil portrait which has been preserved as the only known picture of Elizabeth in her teens.

When the long convalescence was over, Elizabeth wrote Bro that the time had not been wasted. She had memorized some three hundred lines of Greek verse. But of more value than this feat was her awakening to her own youthful self-centeredness, and a budding appreciation of others—her first step toward maturity.

In the phaeton which was carrying them both to have lunch with Sir Uvedale and Lady Caroline, nineteen-year-old Elizabeth sat beside her mother, absorbed in her own thoughts. Above the fringed edge of Mary Barrett's parasol she could see one small round cloud, the last of a towering procession swept by last night's tempest over the Malvern hills. In the immensity of blue sky it looked little and lost.

It reminded Elizabeth of three-year-old Alfred, trailing unnoticed in the boisterous wake of older brothers. Alfred was Mamma's pet now, as Mary, the little sister who had died, had been. It was her mother's way, Elizabeth reflected, to love most deeply the children to whom Papa was least attentive. How quickly Septimus (named so because he was the seventh boy, although Mamma's eleventh child), had captivated Papa with his charm.

Mary Barrett stirred, but not under discomfort of her daughter's gentle scrutiny. She had been lost in her own reflections. Searching the velvet reticule in her lap, she unfolded a paper on which a child's hand had scrawled a four-legged creature with horns.

"See—" she showed it proudly to Elizabeth—"Alfred drew this for me yesterday. The little fellow has talent, I'm sure. Sir Uvedale will know."

"He'll be sure to say something kind," Elizabeth agreed with a smile. "He always did about the rhymes I showed him. What an encouragement it was!"

"Indeed—everyone needs encouragement." Mary Barrett gave an unconscious sigh.

Aware suddenly that her mother needed comforting, Elizabeth leaned forward. "You know, Mamma—your sketches are charming. Why don't you work at your drawing more often?"

In her young daughter's gaze, so often remote and indwelling, Mary Barrett discovered an oddly maternal look. Surprised and touched, she answered wistfully: "Why Ba— I'll try. It's nice of you to care."

Though she did not mention it, Elizabeth was herself bringing a sample of art to Sir Uvedale. She meant to consult him about rewriting her poem, "The Development of Genius," a long, academic piece which she had begun with the overconfidence of youth. That it was too ambitious an effort she knew, now. The hand holding her manuscript under her cape tightened its grip as she remembered Papa's unnecessarily acid comments.

He had been the first to see the poem. But he had read only a few pages when he tossed the whole manuscript aside. "I wouldn't read over again what I've read, for fifty pounds. Burn the wretched thing! The subject is beyond you." No doubt it was true, but it might have been more gently said.

Now she was out of the schoolroom, Edward Barrett no longer judged her work with the same leniency. This fact lent more weight to his praise. She welcomed rather than resented it. How much she had always counted on his interest and help she realized, now that he seemed to withdraw it. Without Papa to encourage, to underwrite a maiden effort, and act as her agent in London, her recent first volume of poetry would never have reached the public.

The book had received no notice, to be sure, but it had taken more courage than she possessed alone to place it under the withering gaze of critics. Together, she and her father had selected the poems to be included. It had been a shared, and to her an intensely important, experience. It made Papa's present attitude a shock. His pride in her made him impatient of failure— and then his troublesome Jamaican affairs were now a constant worry.

How fortunate that she could count on Sir Uvedale! Today, with the understanding patience of a fellow craftsman, he would point out her faults and map out a course to follow which would do much to soften the sting of her father's words.

Only a few weeks ago, Sir Uvedale had asked Elizabeth to check his treatise on Greek and Latin versification—an unusual tribute from a man of letters to a mere girl. Already her gifts were creating a life for her independent of the family. It never entered her head that this was a possible cause of Edward Barrett's irritation.

Other literary friendships were to develop which pleased Mr. Barrett no better. One of them, begun at this period, helped her much later, at a fateful moment in her life, and gave to Hugh Stuart Boyd more lasting fame than all his scholarship.

Boyd was a minor poet and translator of Greek who lived in near-by Malvern. Learning that Miss Barrett was an accomplished Greek student, he introduced himself by letter. Married and middle-aged, Boyd was also blind—a misfortune which earned him Elizabeth's sympathy as well as the diffident admiration due an older scholar.

New acquaintances were rare at Hope End and Elizabeth was very shy. It would have alarmed her to meet Mr. Boyd, but writing liberated all her gifts. The grace and wit of her letters to him charmed him into continuing the correspondence for over a year. His occasional hints that two such close and congenial neighbors should meet had to be politely evaded, however. Papa was distinctly cold to the idea.

But events took the situation out of Mr. Barrett's control, as they often did, to his immense annoyance. Driving out one day with Henrietta and Arabel to pay a call, Elizabeth noticed a man and woman on the Malvern Road. "Why—that's Mr. and Mrs. Boyd," exclaimed Henrietta, who went often to Malvern and knew him by sight.

"Oh, stop, James!" Elizabeth cried impulsively to the coachman, and then, shyness overcoming her, she implored him in the next breath: "No—go on!"

"Goodness, the Boyds will certainly think us rude," said Henrietta, noticing the look of astonishment on Mrs. Boyd's face as the carriage slowed down and then jerked forward at the snap of James's whip.

The only way to redeem her behavior now, Elizabeth had to admit, was to call on the Boyds as soon as possible. Papa's consent had to be obtained first, and it was not granted without argument.

"I can't see how Mr. Boyd could dream you would introduce yourself to him on the public road," he insisted, "but since you are so sure he will think it a breach of good manners, do as you like."

"I do not *like* to go at all," Elizabeth thought to herself ruefully, nor did she have the courage. She persuaded Bro, who happened to be home, to drive her there, and Henrietta and Arabel agreed to join the expedition. The four young people set out, one of them beset by timidity, three of them highly amused at her fears.

"There's Malvern," said Bro as the chaise topped a steep rise in the road. "You girls had getter get out and walk down this hill—we haven't a drag chain."

"Bro's right. *I* shall get out, the pony may bolt," Henrietta decided.

But no one had time to get out. Already feeling the

weight of the carriage on his hindquarters, the pony
started running downhill. Matters were not improved
when Elizabeth lost her head and seized one of the
reins. Obeying the pull, the pony veered suddenly round
a corner and dumped them all out.

No one was hurt, but when the others looked at
Elizabeth they went into peals of laughter. The face of
the poet was grimy with dust, her hat fell over one ear
and a huge rent zigzagged down the front of her pelisse.
The damage to her self-confidence was worst of all—in
spite of Bro's somewhat heartless reminder that "Mr.
Boyd can't see!"

Arabel and Henrietta brushed her off as best they
could, and boarding a public coach which passed the
spot, they went off to an engagement of their own.
Meanwhile Bro righted the chaise, and walking the still
skittish pony, he and Elizabeth proceeded cautiously,
only to come face to face with Mr. and Mrs. Boyd as
they turned a corner. The introduction took place on
the "public road" after all, and instead of being tongue-
tied, Elizabeth was so full of the accident that she forgot
herself and chatted glibly about it to the Boyds.

When they were all home again, no one thought
it necessary to regale Papa with an account of the
affair. His sense of humor was unhappily absent where
matters of decorum were concerned.

After the birth of her twelfth child, Octavius, Mary
Barrett failed rapidly. By this time there was more than
her ill health to trouble the security of Hope End.
Long conferences were held behind the closed doors of

Edward Barrett's study in which Sam Barrett and the older boys took part.

"Profits from Jamaica have been greatly reduced," Bro explained to Elizabeth, "a legal question that has to do with the ownership of our slaves has been decided against us. Papa is borrowing to meet expenses here."

Elizabeth's eyes traveled over the formal terraces of Hope End. "We could live more simply. I suppose we could even sell Hope End," she ventured—faintly, because the words hurt.

Her brother shook his head. "The shock might be harmful to Mamma, in her present condition. She must not be told."

Soon after this, Uncle Sam Barrett left England for Jamaica. It was the first break in a close family circle. To Elizabeth, who had often watched storms form over the Malvern hills, his going was the blackest of the dark clouds that seemed to be gathering swiftly toward a climax.

A few months later a slight errand took her to her mother's sitting-room to find a strand of wool for her tapestry. When she entered, the silence and emptiness oppressed her. She looked about, puzzled, forgetting her errand. She had never been there before in her mother's absence.

Moving across the room, she stopped to look at a glass cabinet full of childish objects. Mamma called them her "treasures." Alfred's drawing of a cow was there, and the heart-shaped pen-wiper Bro had cut out of flannel. There too lay a bookmark, embroidered by Henrietta in irregular stitches, a small rag doll which had been little Mary's inseparable companion, and her own first poem. Smiling, Elizabeth read the stilted lines she had written when she was six.

Mary Barrett had gone to Cheltenham to be under the care of a new doctor, and Treppy had come again, to be companion to her children. Mamma had not wanted to leave Hope End. That last morning when she had said good-by to them all she could not hide her tears.

"When she comes home, I'll spend more time with her," Elizabeth thought contritely.

She found the wool she needed and was on her way down to join Treppy in the library when the sound of galloping hoofs on the drive stopped her. Who could be coming—and why so fast? Held there by growing dread, she waited for the rider to stop and mount the steps.

When the heavy knocker fell Elizabeth opened the door herself.

"A special letter for Miss Trepsack, Miss," said the dispatch rider from Ledbury.

Hearing her name, Treppy came forward quickly, followed by Henrietta and Arabel. Her eyes searched Elizabeth's. Each asked of the other the same mute question.

Treppy took the letter with its black border.

"It is from your father," she said at last, after she had read it.

They stared at her, probing her silence.

"Mamma is dead," whispered Elizabeth finally in the stillness. "That is what you are trying to tell us, Treppy —isn't it?"

✑ *Chapter Four*

. . . anew the garden is deserted.
THE DESERTED GARDEN

FOUR YEARS were to come and go after Mary
Barrett's death before Edward Barrett could nerve
himself to leave Hope End. Bereavement drove him
into a hermit-like seclusion. His stubborn refusal during this time to see even his oldest friends estranged
many of them permanently.

It was his wish that all of his wife's personal belong-
ings remain untouched, just as she left them. Her locked
rooms at Hope End now became a haunting kind of
memorial. Elizabeth could not bring herself to enter
them. There were better ways to remember her mother,
through tenderness shown to small brothers, some of
them too young to know what they had lost. She was
twenty-two, and it was to her, now, as the oldest, that
the household turned.

Sam, Stormie, and George, away much of the time at school and university, would have drifted further from the close family circle had they dared. They came home regularly because of their father's well-known habit of cutting allowances when he was displeased. Bro was bound by all the English traditions surrounding an oldest son to submit to the head of the family.

Henrietta and Arabel were no different from other girls of their period in England. They dabbled feebly in music and painting, hoped fervently for a husband, and were resigned to their own unimportance in a family teeming with brothers.

They were more than elated, therefore, when Elizabeth surrendered to them most of her rights as mistress of Hope End.

"If you *wish*—" Henrietta had begun with the utmost tact— "I like to plan meals and I don't mind interviewing Cook. Arabel would be glad, I know, to supervise the maids. It might give you more time to—"

"Darlings!" Elizabeth was quite breathless with relief. "I never dreamed you would enjoy it!"

Elizabeth longed to comfort her father. His coldness and reserve was really fortitude, she argued. She admired the kind of strength that was like a rock in the face of reverses and of sorrow. Call it what she might, he now kept her at arm's length, favored though she still was above others. Visits to London were prolonged, as if absorption in business was the only consolation he sought.

Although no one at Hope End voiced the disloyalty, laughter when he was absent rang more spontaneously,

meals became gay reunions instead of rituals of decorum.
Even the servants breathed more freely.

Neighbors who had been fond of Mary Barrett took
pains to befriend her daughters. One of these, Mrs.
James Martin, remained an intimate to whom Elizabeth
confided many family tensions and perplexities. The
few who paid formal visits of condolence after Mrs.
Barrett's death were frankly curious.

The new mistress of Hope End, the eldest Miss Barrett, had never been prominent in County society. Her
health had never entirely recovered from an almost
fatal illness in girlhood. Moreover, she was something
of an eccentric—she read Greek and was studying
Hebrew!

They had not expected a brainy woman to be so
attractive. They saw an intensely vital little person with
immense dark eyes that dominated a pale face. Her
heavy chestnut hair was dressed in fashionable ringlets,
her smile transformed her into a pretty girl, and her
conversation sparkled.

Elizabeth's visits to Hugh Boyd, the hours spent delv-
ing with him into Greek literature, made up for the
prosaic monotony of family life at Hope End. The meeting with him had warmed into friendship, a friendship
desperately needed now that Uvedale Price had died,
leaving her undeveloped talent bereft of a sympathetic
guide. Boyd took his place, enriching her with his
scholarship and encouraging her efforts.

These last years at Hope End were saddened by still
another loss. Grandmother Moulton-Barrett died. She
left Elizabeth a small legacy, intended perhaps as the

marriage portion her son was not going to provide. To Treppy, her Creole companion, she bequeathed a comfortable sum. Living from now on in modest rooms in London, Treppy remained a loyal friend but never again a dependent of the Barretts'.

All this time life at Hope End had a deceptive tranquillity. The old happy days seemed to return. Alfred, Henry, Septimus, and Octavius fished now in the stream and the pond where Elizabeth and Bro had fished and brought home their strings of perch and their captive field mice. Elizabeth almost ceased to fear the changes that had once seemed at hand.

It was at the end of a quiet breakfast that Edward Barrett broke the news of their departure from Hope End. Talk around the table had been held in check by his austerity this morning. The younger boys, by means of nudges, well-aimed kicks, and the surreptitious shooting of bread-pills, played their usual undercover game, but even suppressed mischief dropped unnoticed into a heavy silence.

Edward Barrett finished his breakfast and laid his napkin on the table. He spoke with an effort.

"Some of you know of the changing conditions in Jamaica, and that it is necessary for us to alter our manner of living. We shall move in two weeks to a furnished house in Sidmouth. The change will be painful for all of us. I recommend you discuss it as little as possible among yourselves."

They were too stunned to speak. There had been no preparation—no easing them into the shock of losing the only home they had ever known. No one moved while Papa walked out of the room until the door of his study closed. Then Octavius, the youngest, broke the quiet.

"Are we going away for good? But my rabbits—can I take them? And will we have to leave Topsy, our pony, behind?" His mounting anxiety culminated in a wail as he looked from face to face and read his answer.

Elizabeth lived through the next weeks curiously drained of emotion. While she and Henrietta and Arabel directed the last-minute packing, moving like automatons, she wondered if everyone, like herself, had lost the power of feeling. Only too soon, however, the coaches, loaded with luggage, waited at the door.

Edward Barrett and Bro were not leaving yet. They had still to empty the house of furniture and turn it over to its new owner. The gay, irrepressible Septimus, Papa's favorite among the children, was to keep them company. The three would follow the family to Sidmouth in a week or two.

The other children, momentarily excited at the prospect of a journey, played tag through the house. Their cheerful noise was unbearable. Elizabeth stepped quickly into the coach to hide her tears. Through tears she saw the servants grouped on the drive. Not one of them had the courage to lift a voice in farewell. Mutely, the maids wiped their eyes, the men touched their caps.

The horses trotted briskly down the road winding under arching trees. Now it turned in a broad curve that showed the house.

Henrietta and Arabel leaned forward to see, their

eyes streaming, but Elizabeth shrank back. Alone in her room she had said farewell to the associations and memories of many years. She would not revive them achingly—vainly, with a last look at Hope End.

✑ *Chapter Five*

We walked beside the sea
After a day which perished silently
Of its own glory—
 A SEASIDE WALK

A GUST of damp night air, smelling richly of tide waters, blew the curtains of the coach against Elizabeth's cheek and roused her from torpor. They had arrived in Sidmouth.

She had scarcely noticed the picturesque country on their slow journey to the south coast of Devon. The rolling Cotswold pasture lands looked bleak compared to the wooded glens of Herefordshire. Gray stone walls and gray sheep seemed a monotonous accompaniment to a gray landscape. She knew she would never see again the sharp blue outlines of the Malvern hills, except as memory engraved them on the heart deeply.

With a harsh grinding of brakes the three coaches

came to a halt before a large house, distinguishable from the surrounding blackness only because it seemed more solid. Not a candle nor a taper had been lighted within.

The feeble glimmer from the coach lamps shone on the perspiring faces of Sidmouth tradesmen who had followed on foot. It had been common knowledge in the town that the big house once occupied by the Grand Duchess Helena, and left vacant these many years, had at last been re-let to a wealthy West Indian gentleman. As soon as the coaches rolled into the main thoroughfare there was noisy competition to direct the strangers to their new home and solicit their trade.

Willy, the head groom from Hope End, swung himself wearily off the driver's seat and opened the coach door. He addressed Aunt "Bummy," Mary Barrett's sister, who had volunteered to make the journey with the children and settle them before Edward Barrett arrived.

"This here's the house, Mum, if what *they* say is true." Willy indicated the tradespeople with a contemptuous thumb. "You'd best let me and Jenkins and the maids go in first."

Soon pale light from the open house door threw a faint welcome into the night. The servants moved quickly from room to room, setting a candle here, a lamp there. Elizabeth shut her eyes and tried to shut out also the memory of very different homecomings.

Weary hours of unloading followed. Toward morning, famished and spent, they picnicked on bread and jam and tea in front of the fire Willy lit for them in the chill drawing-room.

They slept at last, to the soothing rhythm of rising and falling waves. Elizabeth dreamed she was a child once more at Hope End. Uncle Sam was holding a great conch shell from Jamaica against her ear.

"Listen to the ocean, Ba."

Waking, she saw it was not Uncle Sam but Henrietta who spoke, standing in her night-dress in the morning sunshine, before the window.

The blue expanse of sea and the yellow beaches lay almost at their doorstep. They provided enough novelty and interest to make them forget their homesickness for a while.

The dilapidated old house which had once been the residence of a Grand Duchess was as roomy as it was shabby, and it soon became home in a sense Hope End had never been. Its very shabbiness made for casual living, of a kind they had not known before. Papa came, and after a week of restless inactivity and boredom, took himself off to London.

The arrival in Sidmouth of eleven young people, five of them of eligible age, was a matter of social importance to the town. Soon Henrietta, Stormie, and Sam were plunged in an orgie of polkas and picnics. Arabel, who had no social gifts, developed a serious interest in "art." It was understood that the oldest Miss Barrett went out very little, that she was a spinster of twenty-six and had a terrifying amount of learning. Her absence from parties was something of a relief to provincial folk.

That the young Barretts never themselves entertained may have puzzled their new neighbors, but Henrietta and Elizabeth, knowing Papa's deep aversion to any but a few carefully selected friends and relatives, dared not suggest such a thing. It was enough for them all that his absences were prolonged to a degree unheard of before and that he was neither curious nor aware of their new-found freedoms.

Elizabeth was in better health than she had been for a long while. The gayety and contentment of the others reconciled her to the loss of home. In the soft sea air of Devonshire she was free of the recurring colds to which she had been subject since she was fifteen.

Bro, arriving late in Sidmouth after attending to the closing up of Hope End, was left there in charge of his younger brothers and sisters. He and Elizabeth revived their old happy intimacy during this carefree period. They found that frequent separation had merely widened their mutual interests. The bond between them deepened.

During this Sidmouth interval, Elizabeth was even able to continue her Greek studies with Hugh Boyd, for he and his family soon followed the Barretts and settled close by, as loath perhaps as she to lose a stimulating companionship.

However, at the end of a year, the old house in which they were living began to disintegrate. Luncheon one windy day was punctuated by the sound of tiles being ripped off the roof and hurled to the ground. Next morning carpenters found one chimney tottering and warned the family not to lean on the window sills lest they fall out. Edward Barrett, summoned hastily from London, saw that repairs would be too costly, and as the lease had almost expired, he rented another smaller house in Sidmouth.

"We no longer need so many rooms. There will be three less in the family for a while," he remarked to Elizabeth.

"Three less—" she repeated, puzzled. "Stormie and George go back to Glasgow University of course—"

"Bro is going to Jamaica."

Papa announced the fact as casually as though Bro were being sent on an errand down the street.

That Bro, the eldest son, must inevitably visit the family holdings in Jamaica, Elizabeth knew, but the time of his departure had been undetermined. Like all Edward Barrett's decisions, this one was made abruptly.

"Do you imagine he consults *me?*" Bro laughed bitterly when she reproached him for not letting her know. "In Jamaica, at least, I shall have a little independence— an illusion of freedom."

In childhood Edward Barrett had encircled them in a guarded, happy security. No one had noticed the walls then. No one had felt the chains. Now they bit through the smooth surface of family living to the very core of self-respect.

Elizabeth turned to her writing in her urgent need to forget. Bro was gone—for how long Edward Barrett would not say. The "situation in Jamaica" had already swept a loved uncle out of her life. It was possible such things could happen again.

During the first days in Sidmouth, when memories of Hope End had been sharp, work had been her salvation. She had begun at that time a religious poem—an imagined dialogue between two seraphim looking down from Heaven on the tragedy at Calvary. There were no longer any happier distractions to keep her from writing. She had been deeply stirred by recent events, and emotions, even unhappy ones, impelled a poet to expression. Into "The Seraphim" therefore went fervor and a richness of imagery Elizabeth had not equaled before. It was to prove the best poem she had yet written.

Months before its completion, however, Edward Barrett made a new decision. His decree now was for a home in London. Uprooted again without warning, torn from new friends, sunshine, and the first real freedom they had ever known, Elizabeth, Henrietta, and Arabel looked apprehensively out of their coach windows as they neared London under its pall of smoke. In the heart of the city they were swallowed up in chill yellow mist. Rows of dingy houses and shadowy figures swam in the murk, appearing suddenly and vanishing suddenly like objects in a dream.

Elizabeth shivered and leaned close to Henrietta for warmth. They drove deeper and deeper into the nightmare. When the open door of the house that Papa had rented at 74 Gloucester Place offered them a cavernous welcome, Elizabeth gripped the damp rail of the steps she must climb. It seemed suddenly difficult to breathe in the air thickened by fumes from a thousand chimneys. She paused to rest on the threshold. The journey seemed to have tired her unaccountably.

◆§ *Chapter Six*

*Howbeit, we love this bondage; we do
cleave
Unto the sordid and unholy thing,
Fearing the sudden wrench . . . .*
A SEA-SIDE MEDITATION

T HE RETURN of Bro from Jamaica, after only a
year's absence, made up to Elizabeth for everything. When the fogs and soot-laden air of London gave
her feverish chills and a chronic cough, she wrapped
herself in shawls, hugged the fire, and did not complain. Beside her chair was a table piled with books,
paper and pens were at hand, waiting only for inspira-
tion or the impulse to write one of those long, enter-
taining letters to friends in Herefordshire that came so
easily to her.

Bro was at home and their talks recommenced—long,
argumentative, satisfying, and sometimes secret. It

would have been little short of folly to rejoice openly, in Papa's hearing, over the recent emancipation of the Jamaican Negro—an event which had caused his near ruin. But they could discuss it in private. The subject had cruel aspects which never ceased to haunt.

Since childhood, when Treppy had given curt and evasive answers to her questions about the plantation slaves, Elizabeth knew she had touched a forbidden topic. When talk on the subject was not encouraged, curiosity turned the little girl to other sources of information. She could always draw truth out of her Uncle Sam when she needed to. From him, little by little, and as time went on from family letters and papers and from historical records, Elizabeth pieced together an accurate picture of the slave trade in Jamaica and her family's share in it.

The knowledge grew increasingly illuminating and bitter as she matured. Bro's return from the island, his first-hand accounts of the transition there from slave to free economy, reopened for her deeply troubling questions.

Was not her father's paternal rule a form of the same despotism practiced by generations of Barretts who had used human beings like chattels? Her heart cried out that it was not his fault. The trait was an inheritance—a misfortune of birth, like a disfigurement. Yet what an irony of justice that Edward Barrett's children should feel the yoke of bondage too. Must there not be some penalty for participation in a great social evil?

There were to be family crises when, under the stress

of great emotion, Elizabeth almost believed in divine retribution.

If Edward Barrett noticed Elizabeth's persistent colds and weakened health now they were in London, he did not suggest the antidote of periods in fresh country air. Nor did anyone else. It was best in that household to pay strict attention to one's own business and not disturb the prevailing quiet. Henrietta had a genius for provoking displeasure. Papa bewildered her as he had Mamma. She lost her head so pathetically when reproved for an overdone roast or other domestic mishap that Elizabeth tried often to assume the blame.

Fortunately for Henrietta, Sidmouth friends urged her to visit them, and Papa, whom she irritated, was glad to have her gone, so long as she invited none of her friends to the house. Radiant over her temporary escapes, Henrietta would embrace Arabel and Elizabeth contritely before leaving.

"Dears—I feel such a pig—leaving you in this stuffy old place!"

Seventy-four Gloucester Place was indeed incredibly full of stale odors, mewed up in it by age and the blanket of fog outside. The condition of the houses he took were less important to Edward Barrett just now than a low rental. However, when the Sidmouth incident was repeated in the city, and a falling chimney hurled bricks and mortar into the front hall, he at last began to look for a better-constructed home.

For the next three years he discussed the merits and demerits of one London house after another, demanding that the family be ready to move at a moment's notice, but making no final decision. Summers no longer brought hope of escape to the country and so there were no more periods of release from Edward Barrett as there had been at Hope End and Sidmouth.

Before her health broke completely, however, London offered Elizabeth a few rich compensations. One of these was her friendship with John Kenyon, a Jamaican cousin, who, like Edward Barrett, had left Jamaica for England in boyhood.

Edward Barrett and John Kenyon had never been friends. Thrown together as young men at Trinity College, they went their separate ways from the start. One buried himself in a baffling reserve that looked like arrogance, the other's brilliance and sociability won him a host of friends.

John Kenyon's impulse to call on his cousins now was not due to any tardily extended cordiality on Edward's part. He had heard that Edward Barrett's oldest daughter was an unusual person. A copy of that first volume of poems had fallen into his hands. It showed promise. By what accident had a poet been born to Edward Barrett? Himself a writer of dilettante verse, Kenyon had a great curiosity to meet his young kinswoman.

Elizabeth, Arabel, and Henrietta greeted him with shy formality in the dim drawing-room at Gloucester Place, whose upholstery exuded a sour smell of mildew. They turned a wistful gaze on their somewhat corpulent older cousin. His genial smile was as cheering as the infrequent London sun. Their eyes grew luminous and eager as they listened to his anecdotes of the celebrities he knew.

"Three captive sisters shut away from the world by a grim father," thought the mildly amused Kenyon. "If I were younger, I should certainly act the role of liberating prince to the smallest who is the poet."

For he had immediately blundered when they entered the room. He had thought Arabel was Elizabeth. Her demure poise made her seem the oldest. Henrietta's nervous chatter stamped her as immature, but Elizabeth he almost overlooked beside her taller sisters, until he saw her burning eyes. When she spoke, the shy face framed in soft, dark ringlets grew vivid. Her voice, John Kenyon told himself, was like no one else's. High and tenuous in quality, it lingered in memory long after he had left. He went away knowing he would introduce his young and gifted cousin to his own choice circle of friends.

Not long afterwards Kenyon invited Elizabeth and Bro to a dinner of the sort for which he was famous in London. Wordsworth was present and Walter Savage Landor and other important people. Instead of feeling frightened, Elizabeth found herself completely at ease among the great, as though for the first time she breathed her native air.

Wordsworth sat by her side and talked to no one else while he was in the same room. Landor, discovering she was a Greek scholar of no small attainments, recited two of his most recent Greek epigrams for her special benefit. Her brother, who thought Landor insufferably conceited, carried Elizabeth off to another room to display her knowledge of Hebrew to no less a personage than the renowned Hebraist, Mr. Raymond.

"I never walked in the skies before . . . when so many stars were out," was Elizabeth's rapt description of the evening to a friend afterwards.

It was through Kenyon's kindness that Elizabeth met Mary Russell Mitford, dramatist, writer of popular fiction, and author of one charming book called *Our Village,* for which she is still remembered. Plump, middle-aged Miss Mitford, driven by poverty and her father's debts to inhuman literary drudgery, had been denied many of life's rewards. She fell in love with Elizabeth's appealing frailty and youth, her modesty, diffidence, and astonishing accomplishments. Here, could she have married, was the daughter of her dreams!

Elizabeth, on the other hand, had read all Miss Mitford's novels. Popular fiction amused her and fed a hunger for living which her uncle had foreseen would be starved and suppressed under her father's roof. Out of this meeting grew a devoted friendship. It was Miss Mitford who had the happy impulse to give her sick young friend a dog—the golden spaniel named "Flush," who, in unhappy years to come, was to be a saving comfort and diversion.

From now on, the contacts Elizabeth made through John Kenyon and Miss Mitford drew her into stimulating literary work. She contributed verse to an annual edited by Miss Mitford, and began a correspondence with Richard Hengist Horne, eminent playwright and critic, which in turn led to the writing of critiques and literary essays on subjects related to her field of Greek and Hebraic scholarship.

Yet in spite of these activities and the notice they

earned her in literary circles, Elizabeth remained as withdrawn from London life as though she had been living at Hope End.

Most visitors who came to Gloucester Place arrived at hours when it was known Edward Barrett would be at his office. Treppy was expected regularly for Sunday dinner. The only other welcome callers were relatives or old acquaintances who knew Edward Barrett's prejudices and respected them, peculiar though they were.

John Kenyon was not one of these. He was not forbidden the house, but he was never invited by Edward, in spite of his many kindnesses to Elizabeth. Once, indeed, she had the temerity to ask her father to invite him to dinner. She was curtly refused and did not repeat the offense.

Paternal tyranny, occasionally even as grim as Edward Barrett's, was not unknown in the England of those days. British laws and social customs invested masculine heads of families with authority which bred many abuses.

In one sense Elizabeth was better off than her brothers and sisters. Poetry and the channels into which it drew her were a very real escape, and she alone had a little financial independence through her grandmother's legacy. At various times she tried to divide this sum or give it outright to brothers who needed it more, but since her father controlled the investment of it, it was impossible to arrange this without his knowledge and the risk of his anger, which none of them would allow her to incur.

When his wife died and he lost the major part of

his fortune, Edward Barrett suffered two shocks from which he never recovered. He became obsessed to hold what remained. Marriage would have divided his wealth and broken the family circle he controlled, so he forbade marriage as he was to forbid everything that brought change, or weakened his sovereignty.

The unhappy Henrietta was the first to uncover this mania with its startling implications for them all.

There had been now for months an undercurrent of pleasant excitement at Gloucester Place. Henrietta was receiving serious advances from a gentleman she had met in Sidmouth. His letters required the most carefully worded replies. They had to hint a becoming reticence without discouraging a suitor. They must convey the warmth of a lady's regard without immodest eagerness. Behind the locked door of her room, Henrietta enlisted the help of Elizabeth and Arabel.

Elizabeth dictated the answers, not, alas, because of experience in such matters, but because she knew how to turn a phrase and give it meaning.

The long-anticipated moment arrived, when in the drawing-room obligingly left vacant by the rest of the family, Henrietta's lover declared himself. He had come, he said, to await Edward Barrett's return and announce his intentions.

Henrietta's heart stopped. Beguiled by the delights of courtship, she had kept putting off the moment when she must explain her father and his hostile attitude to unknown visitors. Her lover had come as all their friends did, during Edward Barrett's absences, and right now she had allowed him to overstay his time. Papa might be home at any instant. The only way to avert disaster was to explain quickly—but how? By saying: "My father is a very peculiar person—let me speak to him first myself"? Mercy, how brazen it sounded! She saw she would not be believed, or worse still that her lack of reserve would seem shocking. In the midst of her frantic speculations she heard Edward Barrett's key turn in the front door.

There had been a terrible scene.

After it, the door of 74 Gloucester Place shut on romance forever. Henrietta spent the following day prone on her bed while Elizabeth and Arabel tried to quiet her paroxysms of despair. Papa sent word that she must appear at the dinner table.

Conversation languished during the meal. Henrietta's eyes were swollen and red. In the drawing-room later, Papa said Henrietta had contributed nothing to the evening. They would now expect a little music from her.

Too shaken to feel the sympathetic touch of Sette's hand as he brought her guitar, Henrietta plucked the strings blindly for a moment. When she tried to sing, her voice cracked. The guitar slipped from her lap with a thud. There was no sound in the room after that but her stifled sobbing.

An old familiar agony swept through Elizabeth. In a flash she was a child again, hidden in the window seat of the library at Hope End, her hands clenched in nervous tension while a voice that was her mother's faltered: "I have displeased you again, Edward—"

"You had better go to your room," Edward Barrett said to Henrietta with icy restraint.

Henrietta tried to obey. As she passed her father she groped for his arm and clung there. "Only let me see him once more—just to explain—he left without a word to me—without a word—" she pleaded hysterically.

"Yesterday's performance will never be repeated—not unless you wish to leave this house—do you all understand?"

Henrietta's sobs and the outraged silence of the others in the room were his only answer.

Then, because her weeping tried him beyond endurance, Edward Barrett thrust Henrietta from him in one violent gesture. She fell on both her knees at his feet.

Elizabeth started up. She ran to Henrietta, but the floor of a sudden slanted steeply to meet her. She felt herself plunge slowly forward. A long distance off she heard Bro call her name. Then darkness closed her in.

◂§ *Chapter Seven*

*I count the dismal time by months and
    years,
Since last I felt the green sward under
    foot . . . .*
THE PRISONER

LIKE THE NUMBED STILLNESS which follows
an electric storm, a kind of paralysis hung over the
household at 74 Gloucester Place after Edward Barrett's
latest outburst. Elizabeth was only too familiar with
the lassitude and exhaustion that descended on them
all following a stroke of Papa's lightning.

Henrietta recovered first because she was the least
sensitive. Her pride helped her, too. There was no dis-
guising the fact that her suitor had vanished with
unmanly haste. For a bolder, more ardent admirer she
would have to look elsewhere. Meanwhile she did not
lose hope. There had always been others.

The damage done Elizabeth was not so easily healed. It was deeply concealed, even from herself. The violence of the scene with Henrietta had shocked her unspeakably, but it did not alienate her from her father. All her life she was to confess ruefully her admiration for what was forceful and dominant in character. The Greek gods, the heroes of her youth, had been ruthless supermen, subject to unpredictable passions, able to inflict dire punishment. Edward Barrett was not so different from this concept of what she had first worshipped.

There was inescapable flattery too in the knowledge that she came first with this man of strong will. In return she gave him unswerving loyalty. While her nerves were shattered by her father's displays of temper and her reason told her they were outrageous, she continued to defend him. It was not he, it was the patriarchal system she blamed—a system inherited from Jamaican forebears who had been slave-holders.

Excuse him as she would, the undercurrents of repression at home and the angry outbreaks took their hidden toll of her.

However, a welcome and long-awaited event wiped out some of the dreadfulness of the scene with Henrietta. Soon afterwards, Edward Barrett moved his family to Wimpole Street.

Elizabeth, Henrietta, and Arabel were elated at the change. The Hope End furniture which had been in storage all this time was sent for. It reminded them acutely of a past they could never recapture, but it also made the new house seem really home. Busy and happy getting settled, they could even joke a little over Papa's latest edict against marriage.

"If a prince of Eldorado should come," Elizabeth declaimed laughingly, "with a pedigree of lineal descent from some signory in the moon in one hand, and a ticket of good behavior . . . in the other—"

"It would not *do!*" Arabel and Henrietta chanted the chorus.

"One laughs at it till the time comes for crying," Elizabeth ended wryly.

So began a new existence at 50 Wimpole Street, more comfortable but no less secluded and lonely than that in Gloucester Place. Henrietta found compensations in the music practice she could resume now they had the Hope End piano. Arabel, fairly resigned to spinsterhood, divided her time between charitable works and chapel meetings, and Elizabeth turned back to her writing. She had never sought or needed any other way of escape.

In May of 1838 she published a new volume of verse which included "The Seraphim," the long poem she had begun in Sidmouth. Favorable reviews in *The Athenaeum, The Examiner,* and *The Atlas* placed her definitely now among the poets of her day. Recognition was coming her way, the more easily perhaps because there were so few women then of equal scholarship, or writing with equal versatility and power. She received occasional commissions now to write on public issues. A poem was solicited to help waken public opinion against child labor in English factories.

Elizabeth responded to this appeal eagerly. Her close knowledge of slavery roused her ardent sympathies for all oppressed groups. The exploiting of children by greedy industrialists was a crime—a form of slavery which even Papa called by its true name.

Her "The Cry of the Children" was hailed by the Victorian public as a stirring appeal and a ringing indictment of industry. Both the poem and its author received wide acclaim. So successful was this, her first attempt at crusading, that Elizabeth was entreated to strike a blow for another worthy cause—that of "free trade."

However, when she broached the subject to Edward Barrett, she immediately wished she hadn't. Following the abolition of slavery in Jamaica, tariffs on sugar had likewise been abolished. Free trade had meant the final collapse of Jamaican fortunes. It was an issue over which her father's anger still seethed. His daughter wrote no poem in support of free trade; he saw to that.

In her chosen field Elizabeth had by now won an enviable place. She had become England's major woman poet. Already she had grasped the laurels dreamed of in childhood. There were moments of glowing satisfaction over that dream's fulfillment. But into her personal life at this period came griefs so bitter that success lost most of its savor.

There had come a letter from Jamaica. "Sam," the uncle who had been her most understanding friend, had died. Almost his last act was to leave Elizabeth a legacy. She had never missed his serenity and wisdom more than now, for Bro was in difficulties. She had wrung the secret from him—he was in love. And to marry without funds, in defiance of his father, was impossible.

In the social stratum to which the Barretts belonged,

"marriage settlements" were expected. Members of the landed gentry who went into "trade" became social outcasts. Especially for older sons, who, in England, were supposed to carry on the family name and traditions, the code was rigid. Disinherited and penniless, Bro could not honorably make an offer of marriage to a girl of his own class.

Elizabeth tried to persuade him to take the sum just left her. It was small, but if the girl's family was lenient and added something to it, it might make her brother's suit acceptable.

"Walk off with the money Sam willed to you? What do you take me for?" Bro asked scornfully.

Next she offered to intervene for him with Edward Barrett. But he refused to involve her in his conflict. Elizabeth waited in suspense for the matter to be resolved one way or the other. The outcome was plain, at last, in her brother's grim silences and her father's more than usual asperity.

Under the final breaking of his hopes Bro had no wish to confide in anyone. He invented excuses to get out of the house. Elizabeth suffered for him and dared not show it. The load on her heart was so great she hardly noticed when her breathing grew labored and she began to cough.

One night the stillness of the sleeping house was broken suddenly by Arabel's terrified knocking at Edward Barrett's door. She had found Elizabeth unconscious, her pillow soaked with blood. The cough had brought on a hemorrhage.

Elizabeth's breakdown baffled her physicians and was

never diagnosed with any certainty. The only sure thing about her attacks, from now on, was their recurrence with every emotional crisis at home.

The medical men of that period did not look for psychological causes. They said she was threatened with tuberculosis—she had burst a blood-vessel in one lung— her nerves were exhausted. She must eat plenty of red beefsteak, she must not tax her brain. No more Greek translations—no more reading of *that* sort—they pointed accusingly at the volumes stacked on her table. Elizabeth hid her books from the doctors and stubbornly disobeyed. It was easier not to argue with men who did not admit a patient could die for lack of mental food.

She felt no pain and no great rebellion at being bedridden. Isolated in her room she was also isolated from family situations that had become unbearable and that she no longer had strength to face. Physical weakness gave her some immunity from the pressure of Edward Barrett's will—a degree of consideration he offered no one else. It must have been for these reasons, unacknowledged to herself, that a woman of her mental vigor submitted so passively to invalidism. For when later years offered undreamed of happiness, she was the first of Edward Barrett's family to throw off his yoke and seize her freedom.

So the spring and summer of that year passed and Elizabeth was no better. When autumn arrived the doctors gave no guarantee that she could survive another London winter. Convinced by their arguments Edward Barrett gave in. For the only time, he broke his rigid ruling that the family must remain under the same roof.

In September of 1838 he sent Elizabeth, Henrietta, and Arabel to Torquay, on the southern coast of England, where he had relatives. Bro was granted leave of absence to accompany his sisters on a journey they could not have accomplished easily without him. As soon as they were comfortably settled Bro was expected to return. Edward Barrett had asked his sister-in-law, Jane Hedley, to keep an eye on his daughters in Torquay.

But Bro delayed his departure as long as possible. No one was as close to him as Elizabeth, or was likely to be, now he could not marry. He rebelled against having to leave her, sick, depressed, and alone, with only Henrietta and Arabel as companions, both immature and uncomprehending, however affectionate.

"*Must* you go back—" Elizabeth had whispered to him— "Oh, Bro—the loneliness, when you're gone!"

A peremptory letter arrived finally from London. Sitting beside Elizabeth, Bro told her of the summons home. He saw the tears of weakness in her eyes and made up his mind to stay. He may also, under the circumstances, have been rather glad for an excuse to upset his father's plans, who arbitrarily upset everyone else's.

In any event, Elizabeth's fever mounted that night and the lung hemorrhage started again. There was a family consultation with Torquay doctors. Next morning Aunt Jane Hedley dispatched a message to Edward Barrett. He was begged not to separate Elizabeth from her brother at this critical time. The doctors would not answer for their patient if she was put under emotional strain.

Again Edward Barrett yielded, though with obvious displeasure. His reply was a rebuke to Elizabeth, "that she should exact such a thing." Later she was to wish a thousand times that she had heeded that rebuke and forced Bro to return.

For more than a year her brother remained in Torquay. The respite was good for them both. Summers brought blue skies and mild sea air. Within sight of the house fishing smacks and pleasure boats sailed off and drifted home safely. Bro went on the water a great deal, returning from day-long excursions tanned and clear-eyed and at peace with himself as he had not been for months. Watching him throw off lethargy and discontent, Elizabeth grew better too.

On the morning of July 11, 1840, a red sun rose over Tor Bay and slowly burned away the early mist. By seven o'clock the day was so cloudless and still its perfection seemed painted on the air.

Wakeful as she always was, long before the household stirred, Elizabeth waited for her brother's knock and the few minutes they always spent together before he left with friends for a day's sail. He entered and they talked awhile in low voices so as not to disturb the others. A trivial disagreement arose, which Bro settled with a hurried glance at his watch.

"I think you're wrong," he said, "but I'll be back for dinner—and there'll be tomorrow to discuss this."

To the end of her life she remembered that slight rift.

That evening, Henrietta and Arabel did not wait dinner for Bro.

"He is becalmed," they said, looking out from Elizabeth's windows on a flat and glassy sea.

The evening dragged. Bro had never been so delayed. As often as they thought Elizabeth's attention riveted on her book, Henrietta and Arabel rose unobtrusively, opened the front door, and listened for his step.

"The house seems very hot tonight," Arabel remarked, getting up for the tenth time to look out.

Elizabeth made no comment. With every nerve in her body she was conscious of their noiseless opening and shutting of the house door. She lay on her couch and turned the pages and looked at the printed words. But her mind reasoned ceaselessly.

"He went with experienced sailors—

"There is no wind—they can't have gone far—

"There are plenty of fishing smacks to pick people up—

"They must be almost home—"

Minutes of listening again for footsteps that never sounded, and her silent arguments began once more.

At midnight they went to bed. Elizabeth said to herself: "He'll come to my room as soon as he gets home." She left the door ajar and did not sleep.

The sea was still calm next morning. Bro had not come home.

"Nothing *could* happen to them in this weather." Henrietta's declaration, so positive and sane, reassured no one.

Elizabeth did not answer. Her dread had become panic. Her mind revolved around one useless regret: "I spoke impatiently—as he left."

Hours went by. Neighbors called. The news spread through the town. By late afternoon searching parties were hunting the missing men up and down the coast. Edward Barrett was notified and hastened to Torquay. When he arrived no trace of the vanished boat had yet been found.

◆§ *Chapter Eight*

*I tell you hopeless grief is passion-
less . . . .*
GRIEF

ELIZABETH LAY DYING—so the doctors said.
But she was not to escape so easily. Slowly she
drifted back to vague impressions of hushed voices in
her room, of shadowy figures that came and went.

Edward Barrett's presence shocked her one day into
complete recognition. In her delirium she had called
him again and again, but now, as she lay defenseless,
unable to avoid his eyes, she prayed wildly to die before
he spoke. But it was pity that lay in the stern gaze bent
over her—not anger.

During the weeks that Edward Barrett stayed on at
Torquay he uttered no reproach, spoke no word of what
he thought—that she was to blame for the tragedy
which had befallen the family. Elizabeth felt an over-

whelming gratitude. But the mountain of her self-
accusation did not diminish, rather it grew, as if she
must make of it a monument to his forbearance.

All her father's perplexing reserve, his arbitrary rule,
and violent tempers that had been creating a widening
gulf between them were wiped out by this one act of
generosity.

When Elizabeth's life no longer hung in the balance,
Edward Barrett returned to London. He had endured
two terrible ordeals in Torquay with his usual grim
fortitude: the ghastly wait for the sea to give back his
son, and the burial of Bro one month after his drowning.

In his narrowly religious mind there was no doubt
that Elizabeth had sinned against her brother and himself in keeping Bro at her side. Events had justified
his stand. In her delirium Elizabeth had revealed a
conscience-stricken torment, and he, the only person
who might have allayed it, spoke no comforting word.
He pitied her profoundly, but he thought her suffering
a just and inevitable penalty.

Henrietta and Arabel were left to cope with their
sister's heartbreak which the doctors did not claim to
have power to heal.

For a year and a half longer Elizabeth remained in
Torquay though she pleaded with the doctors to let her
go back to London. The sea that she had once loved now
tortured her with its sound and its constant reminder
of tragedy. Every day that she and Henrietta and Arabel
spent in Torquay added to her sense of responsibility
and guilt for disrupting the family unity that was such

an obsession of her father's. The strenuous journey home was out of the question still, they told her, but she would gladly have died on the way—how gladly she dared not say.

For the legacies left her she was now devoutly thankful. She could pay out of her own pocket the hire of an extra servant made necessary by ill-health.

The young woman in the neat brown alpaca dress and plain bonnet turned the corner of Beacon Terrace and rang the bell at the back entry of the house in Torquay. She was watched by Arabel and Henrietta from behind the parlor windows.

"Goodness—" said Arabel, "she's as tall and straight and stern as one of the Queen's Guards—Ba won't like her, I know."

"We asked for someone who was strong," Henrietta reminded her. "Ba has to be lifted."

"Yes—but she doesn't look too civil. I hope she won't make trouble in the kitchen. Cook has everyone frightened—"

"Including you and me," Henrietta finished with a laugh.

"The young woman is here, Miss," the chambermaid announced. "Shall I send her up?"

Henrietta caught the fleeing Arabel by her skirt as she tried to escape. "Stay with me," she whispered, "she may be difficult."

She was not difficult but she was certainly tongue-tied. They wondered after ten minutes if she knew any other words besides "Yes, Miss," and "No, Miss." In despair they brought her to Elizabeth and left her standing in the middle of the room.

The young woman stared at the girl lying small and silent against her pillows. They had told her she was thirty-four. There must be some mistake. Her sunken eyes were all you noticed of her face. Dogs had eyes like that, liquid, soft, appealing. The old termagant, her last mistress, had the beady eyes of a hen, peering into everyone's business. They were closed forever now and she wasn't sorry.

"I hope we'll be friends," said Elizabeth.

The young woman was not sure she heard right, but she was one to know her place, wasn't she? She said nothing.

A smile flickered over the girl's face. It seemed to light up and warm the room.

The young woman forgot all about "place" suddenly.

"Beg pardon, Miss—" she breathed. "Yes, Miss."

So Lily Wilson pledged herself to a life of devoted service.

While she waited for strength to leave Torquay, Elizabeth gradually picked up strands of friendship she had dropped. Even shut away in a room remote from London she was too vivid a person to be forgotten. Harriet Martineau, Hugh Boyd, Mary Mitford, and others wrote to her affectionately and with moving sympathy.

Richard Horne, the poet and critic with whom she had collaborated once, did much to lift her out of morbid introspection. Guessing that she needed distraction as much as anything, he sent her his most recent piece, an unfinished drama. It was her first call back to the world of letters and the correspondence which followed showed she had lost none of her critical acumen.

After she had returned to London, Horne's warm admiration prompted him to ask permission to call. But the three years in Torquay had been years of mental anguish and too great seclusion. Only an emotional awakening was to break that pattern. She excused herself gently, but with the same firmness with which from now on she kept her door shut to all but her closest friends.

It was in September of 1841 that Elizabeth finally made the journey back to London. As she moved with weakened step across the threshold of 50 Wimpole Street, where sunlight rarely penetrated, she felt no last-minute regret for the bluer skies of Torquay. It was enough to have fled from the accusing sound of its waves and to restore as nearly as possible to her father, the family circle she had broken, first by illness, lastly by a brother's needless death.

For the next four years there was to be no change in the lonely monotony of her life. She was known from now on as the recluse of Wimpole Street. Flush's red-gold coat flashing under tables and chairs to retrieve a ball or bone was the one cheerful note in the room she never left. Blinds had to be perpetually drawn and windows sealed shut to prevent drafts. It is to Flush's immense credit that his tail had continued to wag since the day Mary Mitford brought him from the country and deposited him in the gloom of Elizabeth Barrett's chamber. Yet, for a dog, there were compensations.

There were times when an invalid chose to conceal her faltering appetite from the family, and then Flush devoured the beefsteaks, chicken breasts, and custards left untasted on her plate.

His mistress was thirty-nine now. Youth was gone, she told herself, and except for poetry, life was over too. She could count on three fingers the people who might miss her for a time if she died. They were Henrietta, Arabel, and her father. Edward Barrett's unfailing visits to her room each evening were to her a tacit acknowledgment of his need for her affection. His other daughters feared him. His sons, three of them law students and all of them now entering a world of men, had men's ways of avoiding his society. Sette, once a favorite, yielded him the coldest obedience of them all—just short of insolence.

As for Elizabeth, the doctors promised her no return to normal living. Morphine, or laudanum, much in use medically in those days, was prescribed as a necessity. Her dependence on daily amounts was small and never became an addiction, but it was a private matter as carefully guarded from the world as the violence in family life which broke out when someone forgot to be cautious.

That family life touched her only at the end of the day, when her brothers and sisters dropped in to see her. With them she recovered some of her old gayety—and so successfully that they grew to accept her ill-health as something natural to her—like her books, or in any event as not really hard for her to bear.

Only Flush, lying beside his mistress during the night,

knew when sleep refused to come and how loneliness overshadowed their shared existence. Then with a dog's intuition, he crept a little closer. How greatly she counted on Flush, Elizabeth discovered when he was snatched one day off the stoop of the house by kidnappers.

"I—I can't forgive myself—" stammered Arabel, confronting Elizabeth with the dreadful news. "I didn't think to put him on his leash—it's only a block to the mailbox. He was at my side—we were both waiting for Jane to open the door. When he didn't run indoors I looked around—and he was gone!"

Next day Elizabeth received a dirty ill-spelled note demanding a ransom of six guineas.

"Of course you didn't pay it," said George, her brother, when she showed it to him.

"Of course I *did!*" cried Elizabeth. "Read it—they say they'll kill Flush!"

"Nonsense—that's only a threat."

"You mean you *hope* it's only a threat. I'm taking no chances with my Flush's life."

"Women and their lap dogs!" George raised his lawyer's hands in disgust. "No wonder dog-stealing is so profitable in London."

"Better not tell the Governor," Sette advised. It was a certainty that if he knew, Papa would forbid any ransom being paid. "And *you'll* get it for taking Flush out without a leash," he reminded the luckless Arabel.

And so for Arabel's sake and for Flush's, too, Elizabeth developed a sick headache and was able to avoid seeing or talking to Papa for three days. At the end of that time Flush was home, none the worse, though grimy, bedraggled, and thinner, which last he could well afford to be.

While by family conspiracy many household events were kept from Edward Barrett, nothing could have kept from him the knowledge of Elizabeth's growing reputation as a poet. Yet he who had taken so much pride in her childhood efforts showed little comprehension of her mature achievement, referring somewhat contemptuously to her poetic labors as "rhymes and butterflies' wings."

In one sense she may have welcomed his indifference, since it allowed her to work in complete privacy. Elizabeth, the poet, had already attained a degree of independence, but there remained a personal bondage, a persistent need, since her brother's death, to feel herself reinstated and forgiven. This longing prompted her to dedicate her new volume of poems to Edward Barrett. In the foreword she revived tender memories of her childhood relation with him. Underneath it is traceable the desire to placate and appease, a manner of approaching Edward Barrett, which from long necessity and habit had become unconscious.

⊸§ Chapter Nine

. . . O princely heart!
<small>SONNETS FROM THE PORTUGUESE</small>

A SHORT DISTANCE from London, in his father's house in Hatcham, Surrey, young Robert
Browning sat reading intently before a table littered
with papers and books. He was absorbed in Elizabeth
Barrett's new volume of poems. Even in repose he
looked eager, charged with energy, as though the buoy-
ant life within was hard to repress.

The hand holding his book had an athlete's broad
strength, the fingers alone were sensitive. A tall forehead and strongly arched brows dominated gray eyes
that were friendly yet penetrating. An aquiline nose
gave him a forceful look, but the curves of his mouth
were generous. Robert Browning, on that January day
in 1845, was thirty-three, and possessed of a confidence
and power that were winning, rather than arrogant.

By a curious coincidence, his people, like those of Elizabeth Barrett, had pioneered in Jamaica, though with less prominence. The first Browning on the island had been a cobbler before he acquired slaves and property and married his children into the gentry. With the Browning family, however, the West Indian tie was severed before Robert's birth, when his father, abhorring slavery, renounced his share of the family holdings.

Though an innate artist and scholar, the elder Browning became an employee in the Bank of England, because the steadier income of a business career enabled him to give his daughter, Sarianna, and particularly his son Robert, the education he wished for them. Books were the one hobby he indulged, and these overflowed the house at Hatcham which was reputed to hold six thousand.

As a boy, Browning had been educated mainly at home under his father's supervision. His love for music and art, his marked talent for acting, and his obvious poetic gift were all encouraged. He was fortunate in his Scotch-German mother, who must have balanced romantic tendencies with good Scotch sense. Browning's life in Surrey was everything that life in Wimpole Street was not. Untainted by London smoke and fogs, unshaken by paternal cyclones, it was healthy, peaceful, and warmed by family affection.

In this tranquil atmosphere the young man's genius had thrived and had already sent out promising shoots. Three poetic dramas, *Paracelsus, Strafford,* and *Sordello* earned him serious recognition. The last two, produced by the eminent actor Macready, had only short runs, but they made Browning known to the London public. A group of forty or so poems, published in a series called *Bells and Pomegranates* showed the range of his talent. Two of these, "Home Thoughts from the Sea" and "How They Brought the Good News from Ghent to Aix," immediately became popular. This was no unalloyed satisfaction to the author, however, since much finer poems, among them "Pippa Passes," received less attention.

From the start, Browning was no purely lyric poet writing in the traditional manner. He had a passion for psychology, for exploring and probing the human mind. The drive in him disregarded poetic conventions and annoyed reviewers, who, with some truth, accused him of clouding his meaning with a torrent of complex thought.

The popularity of the woman whose poems he read far exceeded his own. Elizabeth Barrett's verse had by now won her many admirers in America. This new volume of hers quite won Robert Browning too. In a long poem entitled "Lady Geraldine's Courtship," he had come upon two lines that made his pulse quicken. They referred to his own recently published volume in these words:

". . . from Browning some 'Pomegranate,' which, if cut deep down the middle,
   Shows a heart within blood-tinctured, of a veined humanity."

Here was a graceful and discerning tribute to Browning the poet!

"How often I have wanted to meet her—now more

than ever!" thought Browning, shutting her book with an emphatic little snap as he rose to his feet.

Whistling the barber's song from *The Barber of Seville*, Robert Browning replaced Miss Barrett's book of verse on a shelf, and running downstairs, let himself out the house door. If he was to add a page or two to his *Luria* he must clear his mind with a long solitary walk. As he left the lanes of Hatcham behind him and struck out across the open fields, his feet fell into the swinging stride characteristic of him, matching the rhythm of his thoughts.

The winter sun swam like a steel disk through the moving mist. Frost had shriveled and bleached the meadow grass and stripped the trees to gaunt nakedness. The cold was metallic, hard on the face as a blow. But Browning ignored the chill. Something more than his glowing vitality warmed him.

Those friendly words of Elizabeth Barrett's about his poetry were like a beckoning gesture from one whose face had long been averted. Did not mere courtesy require him to acknowledge the greeting? When he argued with himself that he was imagining the sympathy of someone he had never met, he found himself unable to think of her as a stranger.

Pondering as he walked, Browning prodded his cane idly against an ice-covered stream which lay like a white ribbon at his feet. The stick crashed through the brittle coating and instantly the ripple of running water sounded a note of spring. He had broken the paralyzing grip of that stiff band of ice and released something that lived and sang.

He bent over to knock away more imprisoning ice and thought of what seemed to him a cruel parallel. The vital shining spirit singing through Miss Barrett's verse was like this trapped rivulet, held in the grip of a sick— or was it a crippled body? He imagined so, since he had heard rumors of a fall in girlhood. She was a cousin of his good friend John Kenyon, and he had hinted to Kenyon several years ago that he would value the privilege of meeting Elizabeth Barrett. But he had been put off. It was explained to him that she was too much of an invalid to receive anyone.

Browning knew also that she wrote to Richard Hengist Horne and that her collaborations with him were frequent. In spite of those shared labors Horne himself had never laid eyes on England's foremost woman poet. There was some satisfaction in that!

"I will write her myself, now she has given me an excuse." Robert Browning made the decision swiftly.

He had intended this letter of his to be quite formal, an expression of respect for a fellow craftsman, but the results were laughably contrary.

"*I love your verses with all my heart, dear Miss Barrett,*" her newest correspondent introduced himself. "*. . . Since the day last week when I first read your poems, I quite laugh to remember how I have been turning and turning again in my mind what I should be able to tell you of their effect upon me . . . so into me has it gone, and part of me has it become, this great living poetry of yours, not a flower of which but took root and grew—*"

A few lines further on Browning threw precaution to the winds and rushed into a disarming burst of confidence.

*"I do, as I say, love these books with all my heart— and I love you too. Do you know I was once not very far from seeing you—really seeing you? Mr. Kenyon said to me one morning— 'Would you like to see Miss Barrett?' Then he went to announce me—then he returned —you were too unwell, and now it is years ago, and I feel . . . as if I had been close, so close, to some world's-wonder in chapel or crypt, only a screen to push and I might have entered, but there was some slight . . . and just sufficient bar to admission, and the half-opened door shut, and I went home my thousands of miles— Well, these poems were to be, and this true thankful joy and pride with which I feel myself, Yours ever faithfully—*ROBERT BROWNING.*"*

Robert Browning was not in the habit of editing his letters to see if they contained extravagances. With all its ardor and enthusiasm stamped honestly upon it, his message took its quick flight to Wimpole Street, and Elizabeth Barrett read it and then re-read it, only half believing what her eyes saw on the page. Not for seven years had her heart been so lifted and moved.

◄§ Chapter Ten

. . . Thou, bethink thee, art
A guest for queens to social pagentries,
With gages from a hundred brighter eyes
Than tears even can make mine . . . .
SONNETS FROM THE PORTUGUESE

UNLESS he had told her himself, the recluse in
Wimpole Street would never have believed that
her lines could give a man of Robert Browning's prominence more than momentary pleasure—if he noticed
them at all. To her shut-in gaze the stage of the outside
world was magnified, its players cast more than life-
size shadows. The news of her own success was only
news. It made no actual sound. She seldom heard
spoken praise, rarely looked on a new face or felt the
impact of a stranger's presence. More often than she
admitted, she feared her poetry must seem shallow to
those standing in the full, deep stream of life. Her many

friendships by post were stimulating—and perishable as the paper they were written on.

It had been chiefly through Miss Mitford's loquacious tongue that she received news of Robert Browning. From her she had already formed a very precise impression of him in the top hat and long broadcloth cape fashion decreed a gentleman should wear.

Macready's prestige had drawn large audiences to the performances of *Sordello* and *Strafford*. As a consequence, their brilliant young author was in great demand socially. Miss Mitford had itemized with relish certain details of gossip. Browning was still a bachelor and something of a dandy. Romantic speculation had him engaged to more than one lady and London hostesses were finding it increasingly difficult to lure him to their drawing-rooms. Those whom he invited to dance reported that he "polked divinely."

"*And* my dear Miss Barrett," Miss Mitford climaxed her portrait of a man-about-town, "he wears lemon-colored gloves!"

Elizabeth's eyes gleamed with fun.

"I forgive him his lemon-colored gloves. My brothers would all lack the courage to wear them, and, after all —he wrote 'Pippa Passes'!"

To Elizabeth, Browning had become a colorful personality who would always travel crowded highways of the world remote from Wimpole Street. It had been almost a relief when a fresh attack of illness had rendered impossible the meeting proposed long ago by John Kenyon. She knew Browning's poetry well, estimated his genius more clearly than his critics, and this made her all the more reluctant to exhibit herself—an invalid who could only excite pity.

While she never hesitated to approach older men for professional advice, venturing even to write the great Thomas Carlyle, she would have shrunk from any gesture toward a younger and considerably lionized poet.

But now Browning had introduced himself in a letter full of generous exaggerations. Should she be so surprised? Was it not part of the "humanity" which animated all his poetry? She warmed to the picture he had so plainly drawn of an impulsive, unguarded nature that would never count the cost of being too kind, nor, in a moment of enthusiasm, refrain from saying: "I love you!"

That same afternoon Wilson and Flush went on an errand. When Elizabeth was quite alone, she wrote her reply.

"I thank you dear Mr. Browning from the bottom of my heart. You meant to give me pleasure by your letter —and even if the object had not been answered, I ought still to thank you. But it is thoroughly answered. Such a letter from such a hand!"

Elizabeth was adept at turning a compliment. Mild flattery was a polite Victorian accomplishment and hers was oblique enough to charm a clever man. Besides, she was leading up to a favor. Her solitary existence, she explained, shut her off from the reactions of fellow poets, always so necessary to one's craft.

"It is difficult to get rid of people, once you have given them too much pleasure," she edged gracefully into a

plea for his frank appraisal of her work. She would not promise to be meek under his criticism, she might even disregard it, yet she would be grateful to be told her "master faults," which, for all his kind words, could not have escaped his notice.

"I ask for only a sentence or two, in that humble low voice, which is so excellent a thing in women—particularly when they go a-begging!" wrote Elizabeth, her pen poised for a minute over her paper. She could not resist that bit of irony. Masculine superiority was so calmly assumed in Wimpole Street, from Edward Barrett to Octavius. It amused her to speculate on Browning's attitude toward women.

The broad hint he had dropped of wanting to call she answered with a vague reference to next spring when a meeting might possibly be arranged. Winters, she said, were out of the question. Perhaps in the spring— She did not expect him to press the matter. Five months from now a hundred other concerns would have crowded Elizabeth Barrett out of his mind.

Browning replied immediately to her request for criticism. It was an unlooked-for opportunity to prolong the contact, and prolong it he intended to, if possible. Faults of craftsmanship? Why—when a brush "has dipped twice in a lustrous color, lain insistingly along a favorite outline," do you call that a fault? Then Titian was also guilty, said he, in effect.

It was very tactfully put, and Elizabeth, after her first reaction of pleasure, saw that he had touched on an often criticized tendency of hers to say too much. Here she could not help smiling. Her critic himself said a great deal. In a letter, at least, his exuberance was sincere, unstudied, and sometimes bewildering. He took her quite at her word, too. "I will joyfully wait for the delight of your friendship, and the spring," he ended.

It was impossible to respond coolly to such a winning correspondent. With more warmth possibly than she intended, and certainly at greater length, Elizabeth answered. But after several closely written pages she came to herself with a start. Apologizing for her "tedious writing," Miss Barrett in Wimpole Street came to a stop, "out of consideration" for the poet in Surrey. Whereupon a fervent denial arrived speedily.

"God knows," wrote the poet, "I do not know what will help me more than hearing from you," unless, he suggested in hurried afterthought, writing tired her?

Letters were her main distraction, Elizabeth protested quickly. "I have done my talking by post of late years —as people shut up in dungeons take up with scrawling mottoes on the walls." Their small flurry of self-consciousness over, messages traveled back and forth regularly; so regularly, that the devoted and discreet Wilson began to notice certain fat letters she brought up daily to Miss Barrett, addressed in the same firm masculine hand.

The next few weeks fairly flew in Wimpole Street, lightened as they were by this new diversion. In Surrey they dragged. Browning was impatient for the meeting he took for granted. On February 26th he was quite sure winter was over and dated his letter with a veritable trumpet blast: *Wednesday morning—Spring!*

"Real warm spring, dear Miss Barrett," he continued,

"and the birds know it; and in the spring I shall see you
. . . for when did I once fail to get whatever I had set
my heart upon?"

His urgency dismayed Elizabeth. In their letters
the two had already penetrated far into friendship,
described how they worked, confessed their discour-
agements, their hopes and ambitions, spoken their conviction of the other's greater gifts, in short, chatted
tirelessly of themselves, of books, and of contemporary
writers. No other letters she received were so intimate,
so warmly personal and so wishful of a reply. What
might not happen to this enchanting but ephemeral
companionship once they came face to face? The answer
was plain to Elizabeth as the wasted youth she saw in
her mirror. It was easy to imagine Browning's tactfully
concealed loss of interest, but how much easier to spare
them both embarrassment now?

"Dear Mr. Browning," she put him off, *"to me, unhappily, the snowdrop is much the same as the snow—it
feels as cold underfoot—and I have grown sceptical
about the 'voice of the turtle,' and the east winds blow
so loud . . . a little later comes my spring— Is it true,"*
she added, hinting the disillusionment in store for him,
*"that your wishes fulfill themselves? And when they do,
are they not bitter to your taste—do you not wish them
unfulfilled?"*

For a while Browning contented himself with longer
and more frequent letters, into which he unfailingly in-
serted a reminder that the weather was growing more
and more favorable. Meanwhile the correspondence,

despite his disturbing persistence, was having a noticeable effect on Elizabeth. Her voice had gained a livelier
note, her eyes more light. By late March she was strong
enough to move about her room a little. She realized
with elation mixed with panic that in June she might
not have sufficient excuse to refuse to meet Robert
Browning.

How different he would find her from the scintillating, worldly London women of his acquaintance! He
had better be told. She had grown up in seclusion in the
country where there were no social opportunities, she
was at pains to explain. "There are few of the youngest
women in the world who have not seen more, heard
more, known more, of society, than I, who am scarcely
to be called young now." Later, ill-health had deepened
that seclusion. Did he realize what a disadvantage this
ignorance of the world was—especially to her art?

Diffidence and dread creeping into her letters stirred
Browning's compassion. He told her he had been close
to Wimpole Street the other day, and for a minute was
tempted to walk down its length. But then, suddenly, to
walk past her house without an invitation seemed an intrusion, and so he had gone on his way. See how willing
I am to wait, he meant.

April came and went, bringing "her spring" undeni-
ably closer. Still she vacillated. "Shall I have the courage to see you soon I wonder," she wrote on May 6th.
"If you ask me I must ask myself . . . you do not know
what it is to be a little afraid of Paracelsus—" There
were times she wished he would ring the doorbell un-

announced. Then there would be no time to be frightened. How much easier if he took the initiative!

With uncanny perception Browning answered that unspoken thought. "How little you understand me if you think I would dare see you, without your leave." He was going to insist she come the whole distance to meet him. And at last Elizabeth saw that delay only made it harder.

Four days later she took her courage in both hands. She had to. For Browning's sake it was unthinkable to let him enter the house without her father's knowledge. As casually as possible she mentioned the exchange of letters between them and told Edward Barrett of Browning's wish to call.

"A friend of Kenyon's, I suppose?" He disposed of the matter as briefly as that. Lack of suspicion was one of his peculiar traits. He was so sure of his authority, especially sure since the Torquay tragedy, the result of disobedience which Elizabeth would never repeat.

The curiosity of younger brothers, however, was always alert. That evening in her room, Octavius sat up suddenly in his chair and stared at the opposite wall.

"What's become of Browning's picture? You had it hung there—" he pointed—"between Wordsworth, Carlyle, and Tennyson."

Elizabeth turned red. "How you notice things, Occy! Mr. Browning is to call, and naturally, I thought—I preferred not to have his picture—"

George looked astounded. "You've seen no strangers for a long time."

"Yes—but she's very much better—she always is better in warm weather," Arabel and Henrietta flew to the rescue together.

Henrietta added: "It's quite the most exciting thing that's happened in this house for ages! Such a well-known poet—"

"I suppose he speaks only in blank verse?" Henry suggested in mock awe.

Sette, rummaging under the papers on Elizabeth's desk exploded. "Gad—I've found your Mr. Browning! You're a sly one, Ba, to hide him so carefully!"

"Back he goes on the wall!" Octavius snatched the picture from him and hung it squarely on its nail.

"What's this—about Ba's being sly?" The dry voice breaking into the conversation so unexpectedly stunned them into silence. Edward Barrett had entered without anyone's noticing.

"Oh—the boys were teasing—I thought it best to remove Mr. Browning's picture before his visit." Elizabeth tried to cover her shortness of breath.

"Ba's so absurdly shy—I said *shy*, sir," Septimus lied shamelessly.

"Your sister displays a reserve I have found unfortunately lacking in some members of the family." Papa shot Henrietta a significant glance.

"Yes, sir." Winking broadly at the others behind his father's back, Sette took cautious steps toward the door.

"Goodnight, Ba." They rose in turn, careful not to make too hasty an exit, but eager to leave, now the paternal visit had begun.

"Well—" whispered Arabel as soon as she and Henrietta were in the corridor, "Papa does not *dis*approve of Mr. Browning—how fortunate!"

The stage was set. Fifty Wimpole Street was prepared for Browning's entrance. Elizabeth wrote him to come, insisting to the end: *"There is nothing to see in me; nor to hear in me—I never learnt to talk as you do in London . . . if I write all this egotism it is for shame; I feel ashamed of having made a fuss about what is not worth it; and you are extravagant in caring so for a permission, which will be nothing to you afterwards—"*

On the third Tuesday in May, Robert Browning stood at last at the open door of Elizabeth's room.

The woman he had waited so long to see lay on her sofa, the soft folds of a bright India shawl thrown about her for warmth. She looked chalk-white against its flaming colors. Browning stood motionless an instant. For once in his life his imagination had not played him false. The eager flame in that pale face, the quick welcoming gesture, all seemed familiar to him—even the unquenchable youth and fragility.

"Mr. Browning—I should have known you anywhere!" Her high clear voice broke the silence. In three strides he was at her side, holding her hand firmly in a grasp that was warmly communicative, intimate. He had rehearsed a few words to put her at her ease, and stood silent, confused, because her wide eyes looked straight through him.

Elizabeth laughed.

"I thought it was I who was going to be tongue-tied, not you, Mr. Browning. I suspect you of playing a part."

"It is you who have been playing a part," retorted Browning, dropping into a chair beside her. "You have done your best to make me believe I should find a half-extinguished lamp when I came. Do you know how impossible it is, Miss Barrett, for you to quench your light?"

The clock on the mantelpiece struck four. Elizabeth heard it only because the strokes interrupted her visitor in the middle of a sentence.

"I have been here an hour and a half already," lamented Browning, getting to his feet. "How the hands race around the clock's face in your room, Miss Barrett! I have left a thousand things unsaid—and now they must all wait. I cannot risk tiring you."

She had not heard the clock strike since—not once, because her ear was filled, long after Browning had left, with the richness of his laugh and because in some mysterious way he seemed to have remained.

Wilson knocked and entered with tea. She drew heavy curtains before the windows, brought a lighted lamp, replenished the fire. Elizabeth did not stir. Alert beside the tea-table, Flush watched the cookie plate. He was used to waiting for his mistress to come out of her silences—but today he could smell macaroons! He rolled imploring eyes at Wilson. She looked at him unmoved. "You're getting to be a fat, spoiled little dog," was her wordless rebuke. Flush tucked his dripping tongue into his mouth and tried the effect of a tortured yelp.

"I shan't read yet awhile, Wilson," said Elizabeth, roused out of her trance, "you may put out the lamp.

The firelight will be sufficient." Then she gave Flush his macaroon.

Henrietta came in softly.

"Are you asleep? Did Mr. Browning tire you? He left promptly, so Wilson told me."

"He did nothing of the sort—" Elizabeth's laugh had an unaccustomed ring, "he never went away. I cannot make him leave!"

Hours later, yielding to a sudden impulse, she told her father the same thing.

"I suppose it's because I'm so unused to strangers, but the idea of Mr. Browning does beset me—it haunts me —it is a *persecution!*"

And Edward Barrett, blind as usual to what was happening under the surface of the world he dominated, saw nothing significant in this remark.

"Hardly grateful—is it?—to use such a word toward a friend," was his only comment.

◄§ *Chapter Eleven*

. . . and canst thou think and bear
To let thy music drop here unaware
In folds of golden fulness at my door?
SONNETS FROM THE PORTUGUESE

THROUGH THE PALE RADIANCE of a long
May twilight Robert Browning journeyed home
after his visit to Wimpole Street. Friends had pressed
him with invitations, as they always would when he
came to London. There had been a half-promise to dine
out, another to look in on an evening of dancing. But
suddenly he had known he would do none of these
things. He wanted nothing so much as to be left alone.

He climbed to a seat on top of the coach bound for
Surrey, hoping the chill of oncoming dusk would drive
passengers inside and give him solitude. He needed
breathing space. Even the sky's high roof seemed too
low for his mounting elation.

Oblivious of the meadow scents and the white froth-
ing blossoms on hawthorn, apple, and pear, he sat
recalling and savoring his day. He had set out from
London that morning in triumph for his long-dreamed-
of visit with Elizabeth Barrett. Very sure of himself he
was—until he rang the bell of 50 Wimpole Street. Then,
all at once doubt extinguished his joy. Dreams were
never meant to be invaded. Had she not said so herself?
Why had he brushed aside her warning? Now it was too
late and here he stood, on the door sill of disenchant-
ment perhaps!

The door opened and a servant led him past rooms
filled with heavy, ornate furnishings, relics of the Barretts' opulent days at Hope End. Everything he saw
looked depressingly middle-class and dull. Swallowing
his dismay he followed on, up a flight of stairs, down a
dark corridor to another door, a fateful door which
opened silently.

How frail she had seemed bundled in rugs and shawls
but how vividly her spirit shone through! The thought
"half angel, half bird" occurred to him, words to be
stamped on his poet's memory and set in one of his
finest love lyrics.

What had he and Elizabeth Barrett talked of? Why—
he himself had done most of the talking, he suddenly
remembered, and he had come away with his sense of
triumph restored. He had done right after all not to
hesitate. In Wimpole Street he had found something
better than his dream! Led on by the quick sympathy
lighting her face, his impulse had been to describe all
that was dear to him—his family, the warm affectionate

life at Hatcham, the book-littered room where he worked. It was she who had seemed to ask for more and more—or did he misread the shine in those bright watching eyes? Was there a gleam of mockery which eluded him while he was enjoying himself?

Heavens! Browning's elation collapsed. Had he talked too loud? They teased him occasionally about that at home—that and his confounded energy. No doubt he had talked too loud and too long for an invalid. Miss Barrett must be wilted with fatigue!

The coach jolted to a stop where the road to Hatcham crossed the post road. Browning swung himself off and strode homewards, his discomfiture rising, tortured by the conviction that he had been an insufferable bore. Back in his room he paced the floor till worry drove him to his desk. There he sat down hastily and wrote to Elizabeth:

"I trust to you for a true account of how you are—if tired, if not tired, if I did wrong in anything . . . For instance—just what strikes me—they all say here I speak very loud (a trick caught from having often to talk to a deaf relative of mine). And did I stay too long?" He hoped, he said, to be allowed to come again from time to time, but his "great happiness" must not be bought at her expense.

There was something touching to Elizabeth about his need to know immediately what impression he had made—this Browning to whom London doors opened so easily. It did not occur to him that she was starved for the sort of companionship he offered. He had, evidently, no conceits—only warm impulses. She had made him angry only the other day by calling his interest "kind." It humiliated him, he declared, to have her write so when he was merely pleasing himself.

So Elizabeth answered that he had done "everything right" during his visit and "nothing wrong" and that if there had been any "loud speaking" she did not hear it. "It must obviously and naturally be delightful to me to receive you here when you like to come, and it cannot be necessary for me to say so in set words—believe it of your friend—" she ended.

Browning drew a deep breath of relief on receiving this reply and then rushed into the one misstep he was ever to be guilty of in his relations with Elizabeth. He had been terribly afraid he had exhausted his welcome in Wimpole Street. Now he flew to the other extreme. Without waiting for his over-full heart to quiet, he poured it out in a letter so ardent that Elizabeth was shaken.

She had, on her side, expected a sobered Browning, once he saw her shorn of the attractions he imagined. Instead, here were passionate words that amounted to an avowal of love! For two days she was silent. Her only possible answer seemed so unbearably hard to write. It was an unusually long interim between letters and Browning had time to feel uneasy and to question the wisdom of what he had done.

In her torment, Elizabeth came back always to one bitter necessity. She must feign coolness, reject a gift which in happier circumstances she would have embraced. Even the six-years' difference between them which she frankly admitted, was no barrier, had she been a well woman. She had too often seen pity in the eyes of those who visited her sick-room to imagine Browning's ardor could be born of anything else. She must not let him deceive himself—or her.

At last she took up her pen.

"I intended to write you last night and this morning, and could not,—you do not know what pain you have given me in speaking so wildly. And if I disobey you, my dear friend, in speaking . . . of your wild speaking, I do it not to displease you, but to be in my own eyes and before God, a little more worthy, or less unworthy of a generosity from which I recoil by instinct.

"You have said some intemperate things," she said firmly, *"fancies,—which you will not say over again, nor unsay, but* forget at once *and* for ever, . . . *and which will die out between* you and me alone, *like a misprint between you and the printer. And this you will do* for my sake *who am your friend . . . and this I ask, because it is a condition necessary to our future liberty of intercourse."*

Hidden in that last phrase was Elizabeth's knowledge of Edward Barrett and what he might do if he ever suspected the contents of Browning's letter. Meantime she would not complicate matters by speaking of her father. If she was firm enough she need not. She would simply not receive Browning again unless he gave his word never to revive the subject, and this she made clear.

Her answer must have baffled him, for on every page was unspoken longing for the thing she renounced, and the forlorn hope that he would read between the lines. "You are not displeased with me," she begged at the end, "I do not write as I might of some words of yours, but you know that I am not a stone, even if silent like one. And if in the *unsilence,* I have said one word to vex you, pity me for having had to say it—"

Reminding him that he had promised to "judge" some of her poems at his next visit, she hoped he would not mind putting off that visit for a week. Relatives were arriving unexpectedly from Torquay. Was their coming a convenient excuse, Browning wondered? Anyway, it gave them both time to recover, and him time to curse his stupidity roundly. What an impetuous letter! Not that he regretted saying what he had, but he had said it too soon, for even ordinary standards of propriety. And Elizabeth Barrett was no ordinary woman, she was England's major poetess, whose precarious health kept her in seclusion. Would he be admitted to that privacy again?

There seemed to Browning only one way to get back to the old easy footing of their correspondence. He must make light of the whole incident—wipe out the impression he had given of unstable emotions. Through the confusion and embarrassment of the letter he sent, one sentence and its meaning stood out plainly, more so than he intended. "Will you think me very brutal," he wrote, "if I tell you I could almost smile at your misapprehension of what I meant to write?" It was hardly the most tactful way to relinquish the role of lover!

Vanity had long since died in Elizabeth, along with much that was young and hopeful. With perfect grace she accepted his implication that she had imagined the whole situation. "I owe you the most humble of apologies, dear Mr. Browning," she began smoothly, "for having spent so much solemnity on so simple a matter, and I hasten to pay it." But she allowed herself a few defensive statements just the same—faintly ironic ones: the obscurity of his language—his habit of speaking in superlatives, were, no doubt, responsible. However— "I assure you that I never made such a mistake (I mean of over-seriousness to indefinite compliments), no never in my life before."

Because he offered to burn his offending letter, she enclosed it, with the request that he destroy her reply to it. "After which," she suggested, "you will do me the last kindness of forgetting all this exquisite nonsense."

Obediently, Browning burned his love letter, but her answer he treasured too deeply. It remains today the only record of his impulsive wooing. Thankful that he had got himself into no worse difficulties, he confirmed the date of his next visit with a touch of humor.

"Enter R.B.—next Wednesday—as boldly as he suspects most people do, just after they have been soundly frightened!"

⮜ *Chapter Twelve*

Go from me. Yet I feel that I shall stand
Henceforward in thy shadow.
SONNETS FROM THE PORTUGUESE

BY NEXT WEDNESDAY, however, Elizabeth was
forced to put Browning off a second time. Aunt
Hedley, whose visit was not after all an invention,
prolonged her stay with the Barretts.

Perhaps the delay was not unwelcome to Elizabeth;
she was still struggling for a composure she had lost.
Her turmoil had been difficult to hide from Arabel, who
shared her room at night. She had even feared to fall
asleep lest her troubled dreaming reveal what lay on her
heart. In the Barrett household one did not involve
others in so clandestine an affair as a love letter.

For this second meeting, the poet in Surrey had
vowed to show Miss Barrett a detached and impersonal
Robert Browning, so dedicated to general topics that

she would never again fear his too personal warmth. But the minute he entered her room detachment seemed an excruciating discipline! Beneath every casually spoken word lay the memory of unforgettable ones. Elizabeth had read but once that letter she felt he would some day regret having written, yet there were phrases in it she would remember till she died.

With fastidious promptness Browning rose, this time on the stroke of the hour. Looking up at him, Elizabeth felt a humorous kind of despair.

"What a futile gesture of leave-taking, for him to walk out of this room," she thought. "I know now, I shall never be rid of him!"

"I may come again—and when?" Browning asked. He held his stick and lemon-colored gloves stiffly in front of him, unconscious that his voice entreated and that his gaze was anything but detached.

"*Must* I name this day or that for your visit?" Elizabeth protested. "I am forced to think then, you come because I appoint a time."

"There is only one reason I come—surely you know that—" cried Browning, and in the awkward pause that followed he could have bitten out his tongue.

To ease his embarrassment she suggested a day, but her next letter was quite determined. She hoped he would forgive her insisting on the point, but she must ask him to choose his own time for calling. He was a person of "quick impulses," she reminded him, "like all imaginative persons," and although such an arrangement might suit him now, she saw it leading to inevitable embarrassments. She never expected or invited anyone's visit. Even members of her family dropped in on her only when it happened to be convenient. What she could not tell him was that the lesson learned at Torquay must never be unlearned. She would never clutch at any loyalty again, but hold it lightly in her open palm.

The strain of their second meeting over, they turned with relief to the safe ground of common literary interests. Once more letters traveled back and forth almost daily, in spite of the fact that Browning rang the door bell without fail, once a week. In the very regularity of his visits Elizabeth began to see danger. Browning had acquaintances in the neighborhood; if it was noticed how often he came to No. 50 and idle gossip reached Edward Barrett's ears, there would be a quick end to both letters and visits.

The problem of impressing Browning with the importance of keeping their friendship a strictly private matter was delicate. As diplomatically as possible she asked him not to speak of his visits to her. With the exception of relatives, it had never been her habit to receive any man, she explained. There were numbers of people in whose minds the news of her receiving him regularly might arouse curiosity. Perhaps he could better realize the need for discretion from "the awful statistical fact" that there were living in London at that moment some forty odd connections of the Barrett family!

Elizabeth was making an effort to treat the matter lightly and to avoid the humiliating truth that Browning's visits to Wimpole Street were entirely dependent on her father's whim. As it happened, her request for

secrecy did not surprise Browning particularly. Chival-
rous Victorian codes closely guarded a woman's privacy.
Meanwhile, if members of the household thought there
was something unusual in Browning's unfailing appear-
ances, they kept their own counsel and Edward Barrett
remained as complacently unaware as before of the
growing intimacy.

Elizabeth found herself recovering a forgotten gayety.
For the delight of conjuring up Browning's hearty laugh
she wrote him everything amusing that happened.

*"I had a newspaper . . . sent to me yesterday from
America, addressed to—just my name—poetess, London! Think of the simplicity of those wild Americans in
calculating that people in general here in England know
what a poetess is!"*

Since their first meeting six weeks ago, a mysteriously
vitalizing current called happiness was communicated
from Browning to Elizabeth. Besides the secret exhilara-
tion of his weekly visit, the postman's step on the pavement brought a flush of anticipation to her cheeks every
day; exciting work—because shared with Browning—
filled every spare minute. Browning was completing
The Flight of the Duchess and bringing pages to her as
he finished them. It was no wonder that in July she was
well enough to leave her room and take her first drive
in several years.

Elated by this sign of improvement, Browning, in
carefully chosen words, as though wary of showing too
deep a concern, urged her to repeat the outing often.
It was only because the little excursion was so unaccus-

tomed that it fatigued her. Her growing strength was so visible that Jane Hedley, once more in London, made a disturbing proposal to Edward Barrett.

"Elizabeth may never be as well as this again," she remarked, "now, if ever, a journey could be undertaken without risk. Given a winter of sunshine and warmth she might come home a changed person."

Instantly she sensed withdrawal in Edward Barrett's manner. She should have remembered his abhorrence to change—even change for the better!

"Naturally—" her brother-in-law cleared his throat evasively—"some such plan has often occurred to me. However, a journey *does* entail risk for anyone as quickly affected by weather as Elizabeth."

"That's just it—these dreadful English winters do her great harm." Aunt Hedley took advantage of this admission. "The doctors all say as much."

"Elizabeth has a senseless aversion to red meat and port—the best possible tonics for her condition. The doctors indulge her in these whims too much for me to have confidence in their judgments."

Jane Hedley had heard this theory of Edward Barrett's so often that she disposed of it with a curt nod. "Alexandria, of course, might be even better than Malta," she went on, precisely as though he were in complete agreement with her. "There are sure to be more reliable doctors there, too." She remembered to be more ingratiating as she rose. "I know how eager you must be to send Elizabeth away while her condition makes it possible."

Edward Barrett fixed a polite but detached gaze on

a point above his sister-in-law's head as he accompanied her to the front door. He did not answer.

"Mercy—" Jane Hedley shivered as she left the house—"what an inflexible spirit—I believe his mind is already made up—but how, we shan't know till the last minute!"

To her credit, Mrs. Hedley did not give up. Since someone would have to accompany Elizabeth, she won Henrietta, Arabel, and George to the idea before Edward Barrett's opposition could intimidate them. To Elizabeth she spoke cautiously of the plan. The decision of course must rest with her father, but his consent was to be expected.

Elizabeth carefully disguised her lack of enthusiasm for the trip. Alexandria would put two seas between herself and England—hundreds of miles between herself and Browning! Once before, when a winter abroad was suggested, her condition made the journey impossible. She had not greatly cared then whether she lived or died. How perverse life was! Now she wanted to stay, now the deepest happiness she had ever known was to be found in London, there was no obstacle to her leaving. Once her relationship with Browning was interrupted, how she would miss it! And what numbers of people, with stronger claim to his time than she, would immediately fill his days! She had known this always. It was right and inevitable. The novelty of their friendship was bound to wear off, the intensity of a poet's impressions burned themselves out. But the end seemed to be approaching cruelly soon!

The plan to winter in Alexandria or Malta was, how-

ever, still nebulous. Wisely, Elizabeth made the most
of the present. She was of real use to Browning at the
moment. *Luria,* which he had dropped temporarily, was
giving him difficulties. Her glowing encouragement and
understanding of his craft were invaluable to a young
poet only half beginning to use his powers, and more
often disheartened by the caustic comment of London
critics than he cared to admit. He was charmed by Miss
Barrett's praise, of course, though he pretended to think
her too generous and called her besetting sin "over-
pleasure in pleasing."

It was only casually, at the end of a long, half-banter-
ing defense of herself as an honest critic, that Elizabeth
wrote him of the proposed trip which might take her
from London in the autumn. In view of it he must "make
speed" to complete his "Duchess" before she left, and
bring her as many other poems as possible. She would
not be leaving, in any case, she said, before September
or October, "though I suppose I shall not be much consulted." This hidden reference to Edward Barrett's autocratic ways made no impression on Browning at the
time, since he knew nothing of them.

He was delighted that she was well enough to consider such a trip and made no secret of it. "You may
get well through God's goodness—with persevering patience, surely—and this winter abroad—which you must
get ready for now, every sunny day, will you not?" he
insisted, implying that she must develop strength by
going out in fine weather more often. The reluctance
he sensed in her he attributed to an invalid's inertia.

Maneuvering Edward Barrett with skill, Aunt Hedley

finally extracted a grudging admission from him that he would look more favorably on a journey to Pisa than to Malta or Alexandria, but she got no further. All this was relayed to Elizabeth, to whom her father had not yet mentioned even the idea of a trip. Sensitive that her going would again disrupt his family life, she could not bring herself to speak of it, although she had begun to anticipate the change and wish for it.

Browning had spent several months in Italy. No doubt, on his weekly visits to Elizabeth, he spoke enthusiastically of the country and his enthusiasm was always infectious. Then too, he cared so evidently and so deeply that she should seize this chance to get better, that she began to care too. When the possibility of her staying in Pisa was broached he declared that he himself would most certainly plan to spend some time there, thus presenting Elizabeth with another dilemma.

The coincidence of his being in Pisa at the same time as herself, the news of it trickling by various channels back to Edward Barrett, his instant suspicions—these awful probabilities immediately occurred to her. In her alarm she made an unguarded statement about her father that had to be explained—and now she knew she could no longer be silent.

In a long letter she bared the tragedy of her brother's drowning and her feeling of guilt, being careful to stress her father's forbearance at the time. Frankly describing the despotic rule at 50 Wimpole Street, she tried to shield Edward Barrett, characterizing his tyrannies as exaggerated parental affection. "You could not long be a friend of mine without knowing and seeing what so lies on the surface—" she explained the need to unburden herself, and apologized for sending such a "gloomy letter."

Browning hardly trusted himself to answer. That such egotism should masquerade as affection seemed to him monstrous. But since Elizabeth had begged him not to refer to what she had disclosed, it was only possible to say that her confidence had moved him. He sent the briefest of notes.

When she wrote again on impersonal topics he was still struggling with indignation. It was three days before he dared send a few lines, even briefer than his first note. And now Elizabeth, overwrought by the memories she had stirred, suddenly could not bear his silence. "I do not hear," she wrote, "and come to ask the alms of just one line, having taken it into my head that something is the matter."

Still not trusting himself to speak his mind, he spoke out his heart, something she had explicitly forbidden, but the circumstances, he said, made it imperative, "to put an end to any possible misunderstanding—to prevent your henceforth believing that because I do not write, from thinking too deeply of you, I am offended." He had kept his word faithfully, conforming outwardly all these weeks to her wishes, but that did not mean his feeling was changed.

"Let me say now—*this only once*—that I loved you from my soul, and gave you my life, so much of it as you would take, and all that is *done,* not to be altered now—"

Browning came to Wimpole Street hard upon this

second declaration, and Elizabeth delayed her answer to it until after he had come and gone. It was part of their pact to avoid emotional scenes. It was a necessary precaution she never relaxed. The intimacy of their letters was never carried over into their meetings, for two important reasons: to protect Browning and to obey Edward Barrett.

"*My dearest friend,*" she now wrote, "*you have followed the most generous of impulses in your whole bearing to me—and I have recognized and called by its name, in my heart, each one of them. Yet I cannot help adding, that, of us two, yours has not been quite the hardest part—I mean, to a generous nature like your own, to which every sort of nobleness comes easily. Mine has been more difficult—and I have sunk under it again and again.*"

She had thought at first, she continued, that his feeling would soon spend itself. "It affects me and has affected me, very deeply, more than I dare attempt to say, that you should persist *so*—" However, that did not justify her in allowing him to waste his best feelings, by letting him empty his "water gourds into the sand."

"*You are right in thinking that I would not hold by unworthy motives in avoiding to speak what you had any claim to hear. But what could I speak that would not be unjust to you? Your life! if you gave it to me and I put my whole heart into it; what should I put but anxiety, and more sadness than you were born to? What could I give you, which it would not be ungenerous to give? Therefore . . . I must trust you to leave* [this subject] *without one word more . . . while you may well trust* me *to remember to my life's end, as the grateful remember."*

In a postscript she came back to the subject which had started her fears and prompted her to reveal the difficulties under which she lived.

"You were in jest," she said, "about being at Pisa *before or as soon as we were?*—oh no, that must not be indeed—we must wait a little!—even if you determine to go at all, which is a question of doubtful expediency." Thus Browning received his first warning that in this matter and in all matters which were to concern himself and Elizabeth, Edward Barrett's will would raise continuing barriers.

⊸§ Chapter Thirteen

Here ends my strife. If thou invite me forth,
I rise above abasement at the word.
SONNETS FROM THE PORTUGUESE

TRY AS ELIZABETH MIGHT to keep their relation Platonic, Browning's ardent attachment was
more than tonic to her, it was life itself. Happiness un-
derlay the secret of her growing strength. It was eight
months since the start of their friendship and Elizabeth was now walking twice around a neighboring park.
"Which is equal to once around the world," she said triumphantly.

Inertia induced by years of weakness began to give
way to initiative and confidence. From her room, with
the aid of a brother, she marshaled facts about ships
bound for Mediterranean ports and discussed possible
sailing dates. She even obtained her doctor's enthusias-

tic support for the trip. All these steps were necessary before she could go, and it was obvious her father was not going to lift a finger to aid the business. He had not once even mentioned the proposed journey.

This "dead silence" was a clear warning he disapproved, Elizabeth told Browning, adding a premonition that she would never reach Pisa. Browning did not at first take her seriously. On what grounds could a man oppose a plan which might mean the difference between life and death to a daughter?

Meanwhile, Elizabeth knew she must sail before autumn storms and cold weather made the voyage foolhardy, or abandon all hope of going. The income from her legacies freed her to go, as far as costs were concerned, but she was not yet free of the habit of yielding. To act without Edward Barrett's consent was still impossible to her. Memory of the price paid at Torquay for disregard of his wishes was sharpened by superstitious dread. In taking a sister and brother again from home, would she not be repeating an old offense—inviting perhaps another disaster?

She did not dwell on these fears in her letters to Browning, being reluctant to confess her weakness. And then, what if she did not reach the life-giving sun of Italy? She had the present to be thankful for, with its reviving gift of love. All her meetings with Browning were looked forward to with delight. Literary discussions and gossip livened his visits. He was seeking her judgment on new poems and on a possible revision of his dramas. Opening all the doors of his larger world to her, he brought her his letters from eminent writers, in-

cluding some of Thomas Carlyle's full of meaty obser-
vations on life and work.

In between time-consuming new interests Elizabeth
herself was deep in work. The habit of composing with
feet curled under her and pad on knees, as she half
lay on her couch or in a chair, was fixed. A shut-in did
not seek solitude in which to write. She snatched at
whatever golden opportunities arose to break the hours
of silence, and wove her work around them.

Elizabeth sent Browning two sonnets at this time, affectionate word-portraits of Henrietta and Arabel, of
whom she so often spoke to him. But there were other
poems, borne on an effortless tide, welling up from her
famished heart like secret waters bursting an un-
derground source. These she showed no one. Working
over them when the house was empty and still, she hid
them from prying eyes at the first sound of a footfall.

Some were written in a mood of despair. On her
pages fell many a scalding tear, but the poet exulted.
Creative fire had never burned for Elizabeth with so
clear and intense a flame. They were her *Sonnets from
the Portuguese*, not to be shown to the world until years
later, when they would take their place among the finest
love sonnets in the English language.

In confiding her family difficulties to Browning, the
reserve she had been at such pains to rear between them
broke down. He was writing her openly as a lover, now,
and she frankly admitted her eagerness to seize what he
offered, if only circumstances were different. "The best
future you can imagine for me, what a precarious thing
it must be," she reminded him, "a thing for making bur-

dens of—only not for your carrying, as I have vowed to my own soul."

Browning undertook to sweep away her groundless fears. Even should she remain an invalid she would never be a burden. At any moment he chose, he could earn a large income writing textbooks! This, from the author of "Sordello" and "Pippa Passes" only strengthened Elizabeth's conviction that he must be saved from himself. No reply was possible at the moment, because just at this time things came to a head in regard to Pisa.

Elizabeth had finally summoned courage to speak of the trip to her father. All that nerved her was the knowledge that Browning had pinned his hopes on her recovery. "It is all over with Pisa," she told him now, making no attempt to describe what passed between her father and herself, "I cannot tell you how it happened, *only do not blame me*, I spoke face to face and quite firmly—so as to pass with my sisters for the 'bravest person in the house.' "

To Browning the picture of her frailty standing unsupported against the mental cruelty in that house was unbearable, yet he was powerless to interfere. But her brothers were not. Indignation fortified them, temporarily at least. Two of them urged her to go on with her plans in spite of opposition, while Arabel and Henrietta vowed they would go with her to Italy come what might!

Undercurrents of rebellion were so near the surface that even Edward Barrett felt them, obtuse though he was on that score. His irritation flared a few days later as he watched Elizabeth draw on her gloves before go-

ing out. This small proof of health and increasing independence was perhaps the last straw.

"You are all undutiful in this house—all of you!" he
exploded.

Beyond the heart-sinking his anger always caused,
Elizabeth was conscious of high, firm ground, a spot of
resistance built up during the past months, if only she
could reach it.

"Do you mean that reproach for me?" she asked, her
courage mounting with her effort to steady her voice. "If
I give up the trip to Pisa, which seems my one chance,
I must know for my own satisfaction in future years
that the sacrifice is exacted by you—made for you—not
thrown blindly away by a misunderstanding. For I will
give up the plan—out of affection for you and because
my going away once before robbed us all—incalculably
—" She stopped. There were depths of self-accusation
she need not sound again.

He had listened silently, gauging perhaps how much
that debt of hers—that sacrifice of his eldest son—might
be good for the present. His instincts had always been
unerring in gaining his own way. "Do what you like
about Pisa," he flung out suddenly. It was a shrewd
move. Elizabeth faltered instantly.

"Then say you will not be displeased."

"It is for you to decide. I wash my hands of you!"
So saying, he left the room abruptly.

In her exhaustion Elizabeth would have yielded will-
ingly if Browning, by his mere presence in her life, had
not committed her to fight. She wrote him in an agony of
indecision, describing the scene with her father.

*"Might it be desirable for me to give up the whole?
Tell me,"* she implored, *"I doubt about Arabel and
Stormie . . . it seems to me I ought not to mix them up
in a business of this kind where the advantage is merely
personal to myself . . . think for me . . . do think for
me."*

But Browning wisely refused to.

His answer was uncompromising. "All passive obedience and implicit submission of will and intellect is by
far too easy . . . chop off your legs, you will never go
astray; stifle your reason altogether and you will find it
difficult to reason ill. You are called upon to do your
duty to yourself; that is to God in the end." For many
weeks he had refrained from speaking, fearing it might
be thought an impertinence. Now she invited the truth,
he would give her nothing less.

*"You are in what I should wonder at as the veriest
slavery,"* he declared, *"and I who could free you from
it, I am here scarcely daring to write—what retires so
mutely into my heart at your least word . . . I would
marry you now and thus—I would come when you let
me, and go when you bade me—I would be no more
than one of your brothers . . . I deliberately choose
the realization of that dream (of sitting simply by you
for an hour every day) rather than any other, excluding
you, I am able to form for this world, or any world I
know—"*

And Elizabeth, feeling every defense she had raised
crumble before this final proof of love, gave in, though
on one point her self-respect stood armed.

"*Henceforward I am yours,*" she wrote, "*for everything but to do you harm . . . none except God and
your will, shall interpose* between you and me." It was a
promise not to let Edward Barrett come between them,
but there was still the uncertain factor of her health. If
she grew well enough within a reasonable period, then
she would be to him whatsoever he chose—"*whether
friend or more than friend—a friend to the last in any
case . . . only in the meanwhile you are most absolutely
free—'unentangled' (as they call it) by the breadth of a
thread—and if I did not know that you consider yourself
so, I would not see you any more—*"

✎ *Chapter Fourteen*

Let the world's sharpness like a clasping
knife
Shut in upon itself and do no harm
In this close hand of Love . . . .
SONNETS FROM THE PORTUGUESE

WHEN EDWARD BARRETT "washed his hands of" Elizabeth in the Pisa affair, he shattered with a ruthless clarity which left no doubt the belief she had clung to all these years that she was loved and needed.

"I never regret knowledge," she now told Browning, "I mean I never would *un*know anything—even were it the taste of the apples by the Dead Sea—and this must be accepted like the rest." Yet in the same letter she begged him not to think too hardly of her father. "You have his wrong side," she insisted, "his side of peculiar wrongness to you just now. When you have walked around him you will have other thoughts of him."

The other side of Edward Barrett revealed integrity, intense love of family, and a sharp response to beauty, qualities which in the Hope End days were not yet hardened or repressed and deformed. One disarming incident of the later years in Wimpole Street Elizabeth recorded. She described her father walking through every room in the house, holding aloft for all to admire a flowering branch just received from Jamaica. The picture is fleeting against the volume of evidence of a nature grown cruel and inflexible.

Three men loom large in Elizabeth's life. To understand her relation to them one must remember the traditional role of women in her century. Intellectually, Elizabeth rejected the belief that her sex was "inferior," but emotionally she was as submissive to masculine forcefulness as other women of her generation. It was entirely through her affections that her father dominated and undermined her reason.

She had, in turn, allowed herself to dominate the affections of a brother, and for this unconscious possession of another and its tragic consequences she was to repent all her life. In Browning she found the man she had never thought to meet, who, contrary to most Victorians, demanded superior qualities instead of weakness and subservience in the woman he loved. She must rise, if she was not to disillusion him, to at least his level of freedom and maturity.

And so Elizabeth actually engaged passage on a boat leaving for Italy on October 17th. At the same time she and her family were plunged into anxiety. Her youngest brother Octavius had come down with typhoid.

George, the son most in favor with Edward Barrett, had promised to try and win his father's consent for Arabel and Stormie to accompany her. It was hardly a propitious moment to gain a concession, but no moment would have been.

"They may go if they please, but under my heaviest displeasure," said Edward Barrett. Over the lapse of a century this Jovian edict has a ring of absurdity, but it was a potent enough threat to make them all pause. The gentle Arabel, the most defenseless of them all, would be terribly in her father's power if she defied his wishes. As for Stormie, his career as a barrister was already hampered by his bad stammer. His real future lay in Barrett properties in Jamaica, and whatever provision there his father would be willing to make.

There were limits to the risks Elizabeth could allow others to take for her sake, and so the farce of the family's first concerted revolt against the despot in Wimpole Street ended, as it seemed destined to from the start, in ignominy and defeat. On various occasions Edward Barrett had sent his sons abroad in the trading schooners which were now his chief source of income. He was not averse to letting his boys see the world. It was to keep Elizabeth home that he threw this last barrier across her path, knowing the journey was too long and arduous for her to attempt alone.

"Do not be angry with me—do not think it my fault." Elizabeth made a final plea for Browning's understanding. "Mr. Kenyon has been here . . . and he sees what I see—that I am justified in going myself, but not in bringing others into difficulty."

Browning saw she had been pushed to the limit of her strength. With unfailing tact he hid his dismay that a fight so nearly won had been abandoned. Instead, he stressed the gains she had made in health and independence. "Be sure this is for the best; will be seen for the best in the end," he wrote her in a short, comforting note.

In the months to come—an almost full year's ordeal of waiting for him, one fact haunted Elizabeth constantly. Six years younger than herself, Browning was at the peak of his youth. His limitless energies, his love of people, his many talents and wide interests, all unfitted him for the role of self-effacement he so stubbornly clung to. Though miraculously improved, Elizabeth could never at her best hope to keep pace with him. How much better then, she often thought, not to attempt a marriage which must in time wear out his patience.

The forthright Browning, who would have liked nothing better than to declare his intentions openly, hated the subterfuge surrounding his weekly visit to Wimpole Street. It was not to be lifted now that he and Elizabeth were virtually promised to each other, nor was he to be allowed to come oftener, he found to his chagrin. On the contrary, now he was more than friend, his calls were actually unlawful in the eyes of the master of the house, he had to be reminded. Knowing how galling this was to him, Elizabeth threw him a life-line, which, if he wished to seize it, could swing him to quick, unembarrassed freedom.

His decision to go abroad had been impelled by her own, because he hoped to see her in Pisa. Her trip was canceled, but there was nothing to prevent his leaving. Would it not be wise for him to travel, now his new book of verse would soon be off the presses, Elizabeth suggested? Meantime she would wait for his return and enjoy his letters.

"We have both been carried too far perhaps, by late events and impulses—but it is never too late to come back to a right place," she said.

Browning saw through her maneuver. "I love you because I *love* you," he protested by the next mail. "I see you once a week because I cannot see you all day long; I think of you all day long because I most certainly could not think of you once an hour less, if I tried, or went to Pisa, or 'abroad' in order to 'be happy'—a kind of adventure which you seem to suppose you have in some way interfered with. Let me have my way, live my life, love my love—"

Counteracting every emotional crisis which arose between them, the constant demands of their profession intervened to steady and restore their equilibrium. Their temperamental flurry was soon forgotten in a rush to correct proofs for Browning's new volume.

This attended to, Browning urged Elizabeth to accept the offer of an American firm to re-publish essays she had once written for *The Athenaeum*. He took enormous pride in her scholarship, unique among women of her day, but it never blinded Elizabeth. It was only heartening to be overestimated by a Browning whose place in English letters the world would one day put far above her own.

He had become the one person whose opinion greatly

mattered to her. She had been reluctant to undertake the labor of revising those essays on the Greek Christian Fathers, but now she changed her mind and set to work with alacrity.

❧ *Chapter Fifteen*

. . . *"Speak once more . . thou lovest!"*
Who can fear
Too many stars, though each in heaven
shall roll—
Too many flowers, though each shall
crown the year?
                    SONNETS FROM THE PORTUGUESE

FOR THE PAST SIX MONTHS Flush had indulged in periods of moping. His world had
changed since that fateful 21st of May when a certain
vigorous masculine step had halted on the threshold of
Miss Barrett's room, then crossed to her couch in a few
possessive strides.

Fifty Wimpole Street literally overflowed with young
men—brothers of Miss Barrett, whose running feet on
the stairs were a familiar sound to him. Familiar too
was a slow footfall which approached the room every

evening. When Edward Barrett entered, Flush flattened himself on the floor and lay still.

Once these intruders had gone, a comfortable emptiness settled on the room again, the special caresses showered on him held the same warmth. But accompanying Mr. Browning came a cheerful booming voice and the room was suddenly filled to bursting with suppressed energy. The silence when he left was not empty at all. It vibrated! His mistress' hand stroked Flush absently, her eyes rested on him without seeing him. He whimpered but she did not hear. It was clear to Flush that he was no longer companion—only dog.

When Browning appeared now Flush rose with a look of offended dignity and retired under Miss Barrett's couch. This little comedy too went unnoticed. Then, one day, Wilson took Miss Barrett's winter coat from its camphor wrappings, aired it, and laid it on a chair. Flush's mounting sense of injury was suddenly inflamed by the sight of its two fur cuffs. Were they cat or rabbit? Fresh rivals in any case! He pounced on them and Wilson caught him just in time.

Flush's attack of jealousy coincided with the arrival of winter, a warmer, brighter winter than England had known for some time. It was as if the climate had joined the conspiracy to free the recluse in Wimpole Street. Browning, noticing in mid-January how steadily Elizabeth held her ground, rejoiced—and chafed. For what truer evidence of life and health were they now waiting, he asked her? Should she not begin to plan definitely for her new existence with him—work for it, expect it?

But Elizabeth dared not test her new-found strength in winter. A change of weather had too often meant a relapse. What a burden for Browning if she fell sick on his hands! They must take no chances, make no rash moves. Summer was the safest time. Besides, he did not guess, she was sure, how their plans would be blocked if they did not act with the utmost caution.

"From the moment of a suspicion entering *one* mind, we should be able to meet never again in this room, nor to have intercourse by letter through the ordinary channel. I mean that letters of yours addressed to me here, would infallibly be stopped and destroyed—if not opened. What should I do," Elizabeth pleaded, "if I did not see you nor hear from you . . . and then I might be thrown out of the window or its equivalent— I look back shuddering on the dreadful scenes in which poor Henrietta was involved—"

Her sisters had guessed her secret, Elizabeth confessed, but she trusted them implicitly and she had made them understand that if the engagement was broken it would not be his fault. "I made them understand that thoroughly," she repeated, with that constant care not to compromise him which both touched and exasperated Browning.

Henrietta, Elizabeth added, was running the same risk as she herself. She had at present three suitors. Intent on thwarting each other, they arrived at the same hour every morning, as soon as the house door shut on

Edward Barrett. How any of them proposed in front of the others was a secret known only to Henrietta. But their angry disputes were entirely audible to everyone. One suitor finally gave up in disgust, but the second had to be forcibly ejected into the street by Capt. Surtees Cook, Henrietta's choice.

Happily for her, Capt. Cook made no objection to a long secret engagement. His scarlet regimentals cost him a pretty penny, and he would have to wait anyway for promotion before he could afford a wife who must walk into his arms disinherited and penniless. All the humor Elizabeth could extract from Henrietta's comedy she passed on to Browning, hoping to lighten their own load; and he, perversely, was "not amused."

What she revealed of her family life preyed on his mind. He had been bothered lately, he wrote her, with a recurring nightmare in which she and her father figured. "I stand by (powerless to interpose by a word even) and see the infliction of tyranny . . . and I wake just in time not to die: let no one try this kind of experiment on me or mine!"

The repressed fury in his last phrase woke a new anxiety in Elizabeth, that Edward Barrett and Robert Browning might some day confront each other. Next morning, a second letter from Browning did not lessen her fear. "One trial I *know* I should not be able to bear, the repetition of these 'scenes'—intolerable—not to be written of, even my mind *refuses* to form a clear conception of them."

The plainer Edward Barrett's mania became to Browning the more he wanted to hasten the day when he could give Elizabeth legal protection. Soon he was pleading his cause again—this time more astutely. He was consulting his own interests entirely, as she insisted he should, he said: "My only good in this world is to spend my life with you—I claim your promise's fulfillment—say at the summer's end; it cannot be for your good that this state of things should continue."

Realizing fully at last that Browning was under great tension, Elizabeth answered: "If in the time of fine weather, I am not ill—you shall decide. I will make no difficulties." It was a promise with an "if," but she would not commit herself further. "I cannot help looking out to the future, to the blue ridges of the hills, to the *chances* of your being happy with me."

The future would begin badly, there was no evading that. An elopement, to the Victorian mind, meant scandal. She and Browning were too well known to hope to escape publicity and censure. How infuriating the gossip would be to her father, how unwelcome to her relatives, she did not doubt, while the knowledge that Browning's family would come in for their share did not bear thinking about.

Browning, too, had qualms, though he kept the foremost to himself. If the strain of their flight from London proved too much, if Elizabeth Barrett fell seriously ill on that journey he was urging, would he ever want to show his face in England again?

The second involved his pride. He had no means outside the always meager income a poet earned. People would say that his wife's money supported him. His proposal to write textbooks Elizabeth had rejected with so much finality that he dared not reopen the subject. If he must exploit himself, she had said, they would both write light verse for *Blackwood's Magazine* which had already solicited their contributions.

Browning's next move was to suggest applying to the government for a literary pension; but then, Elizabeth pointed out, he might be asked to perform some foreign service in return. If he was sent to Russia or some country with an impossible climate, she would be unable to join him.

"It is not the least importance to either of us, as long as we live," Elizabeth closed the subject for good, "whether the sixpence, we live by, came most from you or from me . . . it will be as much mine as yours, and yours as mine, when we are together—" However, Browning stood firm against her wish to make him her sole heir, and insisted that she sign a statement bequeathing her money back to her family after his own death.

Winter was over and April half gone. The time was fast approaching when Elizabeth's great decision to leave Wimpole Street must be acted upon. Unwilling to hasten a step so irrevocable for Browning, she let matters drift, while he, realizing that the break with her family was bound to be a painful drama, hardly dared press her. He guessed her moments of panic. They showed each time she put off discussion of their plans "because we have so much time."

Since the crisis over Pisa, Edward Barrett had stopped his daily evening visits to Elizabeth, and in this she found relief. His unsuspecting glance no longer stabbed her conscience. She no longer needed to brace herself for fresh deception whenever he knocked at her door. Should her father choose suddenly to be generous, her independence might collapse, she well knew. It was altogether better not to see him. No one else could so weaken her purpose.

With others Elizabeth was neither self-abasing nor timid. She showed so much spirit at this time, in fact, that her friends began to speculate.

"I suppose now that Mr. Browning's book is done and there are no more excuses for coming, he will come without excuses," remarked John Kenyon one day in April, and while Elizabeth held her breath for want of an answer, he pursued the topic with secret amusement. "What are Mr. Browning's prospects in life?" His eyes behind their glittering spectacles probed curiously. "Mrs. Procter remarked to me only last week it was a pity he had not seven or eight hours a day of occupation."

"Absurd!" exploded Elizabeth, "seeing that to put race horses into dray carts is not usually done or advised!" Her vehemence told the astute John Kenyon all he wanted to know.

Even dear Miss Mitford's calls had become a bore because she stayed for hours and talked volubly of this and that but hardly ever mentioned Mr. Browning. "I dare not, even in a letter, be the first to talk . . . of you," Elizabeth told Browning, "if I whisper your name I expect to be directly answered by all the thunders of Heaven and cannons of earth."

By this time all but one member of the household in

Wimpole Street guessed or suspected her secret. Sure that he was implicitly obeyed, Edward Barrett went off calmly to his office each morning and as calmly returned at night, while behind his back Henrietta had engaged herself to marry Surtees Cook and Elizabeth was planning to escape.

Elizabeth soon learned that her brothers were not so blind. An issue of *The Examiner* had printed a favorable critique of Browning's new book. This number was in her father's study for several days before she knew of its contents.

"Now why—" she demanded of Stormie that evening, "couldn't one of you have thought to bring it to my room?"

Stormie turned an inquisitive eye on the once languid figure sitting now so bolt upright. He lowered himself deliberately into a chair and looked her impudently in the face.

"Why, my dear Ba—none of us has had a chance at *The Examiner* since it arrived. You should know who has been reading it—and *he* has very properly put it out of the way by now, to keep you from the impropriety of thinking too much about Mr. Browning."

Elizabeth turned crimson, but she did not fear Stormie's mischievous stare any more than her sisters' knowledge, Wilson's tacit understanding, or John Kenyon's kindly warnings.

"Does Mrs. Jameson know that Mr. Browning comes here?" Kenyon had asked the other day. "No? Well then —I advise you to give directions to the servants that when she comes or anyone else asks for you, they should not say *Mr. Browning is with you*—as they said the other day to Miss Bayley, who told me of it."

Through mutual friends, Mrs. Jameson and Browning were in frequent contact. A well-known critic and author, Mrs. Jameson was also Elizabeth's friend and close neighbor on Wimpole Street. Browning was in a quandary what to say if she brought up the name of Miss Barrett. There was a fine line to be drawn between avoiding the truth and falsifying. Browning refused to lie, but partners in concealment had to agree on a course.

"Does she know that you write me?" he asked Elizabeth. "Never make any secret of that."

There were times when her own discretion failed Elizabeth. A visitor once announced that Robert Browning had been engaged years ago to an acquaintance. "A very strong attachment, my dear Miss Barrett, broken off by *her,* on the ground of religious differences."

Startled and indignant, Elizabeth denied it hotly. Then, panic-stricken at her folly, lapsed into white-faced silence. "Ah, I did not mean to tell you," she wrote Browning, "but it is better to tell you at once and have done . . . it is nonsense I know."

"I hold myself rather aggrieved," Browning laughed, "they used to get up better stories of Lord Byron,—and even *I told* you, anticipatingly, that I caused that first wife of mine to drown and hang herself."

Not less than six days later, Elizabeth tossed him with great relish, a second rumor. "One of my brothers brought it home as the latest news—that 'Mr. Browning is to be married immediately to Miss Campbell.' The tellers of the news were 'intimate friends' they said, and knew it from the highest authority."

This time poor Browning lost his sense of humor. "This last charge about 'Miss Campbell'—briefly—I never in my life saw to my knowledge, a woman of that name—" and he went on to protest at great length his indifference to "young ladies."

In May, Edward Barrett brought home some flowers to Elizabeth. London streets were gay with them. Their scent and brightness must have revived happier days. "They went a little to my heart as I took them," Elizabeth admitted with a pang for the deception she was practicing.

In late June she began for the first time in years to call on old friends. One of them was Hugh Boyd, the blind poet and teacher of her girlhood with whom she had never ceased to correspond. She had not seen him since her illness in Torquay, although for many years now he had been living in London. It moved her strangely to find him as blind, as hermit-like, and as stooped as ever, sitting alone in his dark city rooms "as if he had not moved these seven years—these seven heavy changeful years."

It was natural, as she began to go out more, that Browning should want to arrange a meeting between his father and mother and Elizabeth. Again, as so often, Elizabeth was obliged to disappoint him. Such a meeting would make it appear that they had been accomplices. "Your father and mother would be blamed (in this house, I know, if not in others) for not apprizing my

father of what they knew. I do beseech you to consider well," she begged him for the hundredth time,
"whether you will not have too much pain in finding
that they suffer . . . they will suffer, to hear you spoken
of as we both shall be spoken of—be perfectly sure . . .
think of it in time, lest you think of it too late."

Browning was so upset by this shattering of his long-
cherished plan that he jumped to a hasty conclusion.
He was being asked to conceal from his family (with
whom he was particularly intimate), the most important event in his life. Why—it would break their hearts,
he said.

"*When* did I try to dissuade you from telling all to
your father and mother?" Elizabeth countered. "I would
rather, I think, as was intimated in my letter this morning, have all at an end at once . . . How mortifying
to the just pride of your family, as well as to your own
self-respect is every possible egress from these unhappy
circumstances . . . Ah—I told you—I told you long
ago! I saw that at the beginning."

Startled by her note of despair Browning reversed
himself. His parents were too rational to take offense.
He had been tempted into the absurd fancy that he
must say to them some morning: "I am going away,
never mind where—with somebody, never concern
yourselves with whom—to stay, if forever, is it any business of yours to enquire?" Their difference dissolved in
laughter.

Flush detested being walked by Wilson. Her neat heel
taps on the pavement never paused. There was no loi-

tering at back entries, no sniffing of lamp posts. But he had been walked by Wilson because everyone else was busy, and he had been forgotten by her as soon as they re-entered the house. A voice had called from the kitchen, place of tantalizing odors, and the pantry door had shut in his face before he could follow.

He sat disconsolate on the stairs, limp tail and mournful eyes expressing his martyrdom. Then the front doorbell rang and Mr. Browning was admitted. As those legs he hated mounted toward him, impeccably attired in honor of the most adored lady in London, Flush leaped furiously and bit—as hard as an impeding umbrella and a mouthful of tweed permitted.

"Why—you little devil," exclaimed Browning affectionately, shoving Flush aside and continuing upstairs.

"You will forgive him for me?" begged Elizabeth later. "I slapped his ears and told him he should never be loved again; and he . . . looked into my face with such great beseeching eyes that you would certainly have forgiven him just as I did. It is not savageness . . . he has no savage caprices like other dogs and men I have known," said Elizabeth, who knew whereof she spoke.

"Poor Flush," replied Browning, "do you think I do not love and respect him for his jealous supervision,— for his slowness to know another, having once known you?"

✑ Chapter Sixteen

What can I give thee back, O liberal
And princely giver . . . .
SONNETS FROM THE PORTUGUESE

I T W A S in July, barely one week after Flush's sudden attack on Browning, that Aunt Hedley and her
family arrived for a visit to Wimpole Street. At such a
time the eyes of affectionate relatives could see too
much. Browning came to the house only when the Hedleys were supposed to be out. Even so, Mrs. Hedley often returned sooner than expected, and as she was not a
very discreet person, she gave Henrietta and Arabel a
bad moment one evening, at dinner.

"I've not seen Ba all day," she remarked, "and when
I went to her room, to my astonishment—a gentleman
was sitting there—"

In the act of carving, Edward Barrett paused with his

knife raised. He shot the startled Arabel a glare of silent enquiry.

"Mr. Browning called today," she explained hastily.

"And—" Mrs. Hedley went on, "Ba bowed her head as if she meant to signify to me that I was not to come in."

"Oh—" burst from Henrietta, "*that* must have been a mistake of yours! Perhaps she meant just the contrary—"

"You should have gone in," agreed Edward Barrett, apparently satisfied that no edict of his had been violated. "You should have seen the poet—*Bells and Pomegranates,* you know," he finished with a flourish of his knife.

Mrs. Hedley's talent for saying the wrong thing cropped up again. She was in her niece's room at another time when Edward Barrett came in with a legal document for Elizabeth to sign.

"Is that your marriage settlement, my dear?" laughed Mrs. Hedley. The question was aimed at her brother-in-law, whose views on matrimony she had little patience with. But Elizabeth's pen sputtered. When she handed the paper back she had spelled her name incorrectly.

"Pshaw!" Edward Barrett scrutinized her signature disgustedly. "Really Ba—at your age!"

The constant need for vigilance was nerve-racking, and Browning, to whom Elizabeth related these incidents, begged her to set a time for ending the suspense. Had he played the masterful lover Elizabeth might very probably have leaned on him with relief, but he saw her as one who had been abominably enslaved, on whom he would not impose his own will. It was important to make this distinction between himself and Edward Barrett.

He would never understand, Elizabeth saw, how reluctant she was to bind him to his agreement, and so, at his urging, she suggested the end of September as the time for escape. A bare seven weeks remained to make their arrangements.

Money for the journey to Pisa was needed, for Pisa had been decided upon as their goal. Elizabeth's invested legacies were managed by her father. She did not expect another distribution of income from him before October. The combined resources of both herself and Browning did not add up to sufficient ready funds. Browning was forced at last to confide in his father and accepted a loan from him of one hundred pounds.

His parents never dreamed of interfering in his affairs, he hastened to assure Elizabeth. They trusted him. And then, because the failure of his plan to have them meet Elizabeth was still a bitter disappointment, he added: "If you care for any love . . . you will have theirs—they give it to you, whether you take it or no."

Somewhat hurt, Elizabeth could only protest she was not indifferent. It was a point on which they could not agree—the need to protect his family from "the mud" likely to spatter them all after a secret marriage. Malicious talk, Robert argued, gave right-minded people little concern and Edward Barrett's opinion mattered still less. "How like a man you talk," Elizabeth answered in effect. It was the habit of men to ignore gossip until it struck at those they loved. So saying, she stood firm in her woman's knowledge of the world and of himself.

What to do about Wilson was the next question to be settled. Browning might find her very much in the way, and a maid would certainly add to their expenses. But he, well aware that Wilson's devoted care would be a vital factor in the success of their venture, was only too thankful that she was willing to cast her lot in with theirs. Wilson must come, he insisted.

It was something of a miracle, that, in the remaining weeks, Elizabeth's health and determination did not falter. Friends began to take too personal an interest in her welfare. Mrs. Jameson, usually the soul of tact, grew suddenly insistent that Elizabeth reach Italy while the warm weather made the trip possible. Knowing that Arabel and a brother were forbidden as escorts, she offered herself, in spite of John Kenyon's warning that anyone who made himself responsible for a member of Edward Barrett's family, especially an invalid daughter, put himself in a dangerous position.

Nothing daunted, Mrs. Jameson went direct to Elizabeth, trying to hammer through her silence. Elizabeth hedged—hoped her friend would not think her discourteous—there were "reasons" why she could not explain her plans at this moment.

Only temporarily defeated, Mrs. Jameson tried again two weeks later. "What have you decided about Italy, my dear?"

"Oh—" Elizabeth stammered, "I shall not go away—

not anyway before September. So you see—there is no use planning yet."

It was, at the moment, almost September and Mrs. Jameson's look said as much. "Very sudden then it is to be," she remarked after a prolonged pause, "in fact, there is only an elopement for you."

Elizabeth's laugh implied: "What a preposterous idea!" but she was afraid it deceived no one.

Treppy, the Barretts' old companion from Jamaica, ceased coming to Wimpole Street. Arabel took her to task.

"You are all too secretive in Wimpole Street, that's why I don't come," was Treppy's tart explanation. "Oh, you needn't look so innocent—my eyes may be old, but they still see!"

"You're always imagining things, Treppy."

"I don't imagine what is plain before me, and what's more, my girl, you needn't try to deceive me. If Elizabeth ever goes to Italy, it will be with a husband."

Arabel gasped and reported this piece of clairvoyance to Elizabeth. "How people are talking and inferring!" Elizabeth shuddered in her next letter to Browning. "Not that there is any danger from Treppy. She would as soon cut off her right hand as bring one of us into a difficulty, and *me* the last."

Even Hugh Boyd, with a blind man's acuteness, guessed the truth from one of her letters. Elizabeth admitted as much to Browning. "I wrote something in a note to Mr. Boyd some weeks ago, which nobody but himself would have paused to think over; but he, like a prisoner in a dungeon, sounds every stone of the walls around him, and discerns a hollowness, detects a wooden beam—patiently pricks out the mortar with a pin—all this in his rayless companionless dark . . . poor Mr. Boyd."

Tensions were growing on all sides. Flush felt them too. He bit Browning a second time and had to be slapped again—this time much harder, by Wilson. Elizabeth talked of muzzling him after that, but Browning would not hear of it. Instead he presented his small rival with a bag of macaroons. This artful maneuver won Flush over completely. He devoured the gift and remained Browning's cordial friend as long as he lived.

Elizabeth's daily walks to the end of the block to post letters gave her confidence that she was returning to normal living. But quiet Wimpole Street was nothing like the tumult of the outside world into which she must soon plunge. She tried to prepare herself for the change.

She had not been to church since her agonized endurance of the memorial services for her brother. When she stood with Browning before an altar, would her nerves play her false? To test herself she went with Arabel to hear a prominent minister. The church, she knew, would be jammed with people. It was not the crowd but the organ music that proved her undoing. Seeing tears course down her face Arabel got her out and into a cab without more ado.

Browning, when he heard she had been unnerved, was concerned. He understood more and more clearly the hazards of undertaking an arduous journey with a woman whose health had been completely shattered.

They had planned the trip to Italy by rail because it was cheaper. Now, remembering the rough roadbeds, the engine fumes, the constant racket, and the draughts, he doubted the wisdom of it. "Let us go by boat instead," he suggested, "if it is not too late to get reservations."

But no sooner did Browning have misgivings than Elizabeth grew positive she could endure anything once she was with him. He would see! To sail was impossible, she pointed out, because it forced them to leave on a fixed date. Her father had always been unpredictable. He moved his family hither and yon like pawns, without consulting them. If he should spring one of his sudden decisions on them, all their plans would be useless. Trains were their best chance. They ran daily and could be boarded at a moment's notice.

It was obvious to Browning that he must trust Elizabeth's knowledge of the circumstances surrounding her. "All my life is bound up with the success of this measure," he yielded, "therefore think and decide, my beloved."

"If I am to think and decide," answered Elizabeth, and a breathless haste drove her pen, as though she were already in flight from Edward Barrett, "let us go through France. And let us go quick, quick, and not stop anywhere within hearing of England—not stop at Havre nor at Rouen, nor at Paris—that is how I decide. May God help us, and smooth the way before and behind. May your father be able to love me a little," she ended in bitter afterthought, "for my father will never love me again."

⋙ *Chapter Seventeen*

Say thou dost love me, love me, love me
   —toll
The silver iterance!
      SONNETS FROM THE PORTUGUESE

THE HEDLEYS were at last on the point of leaving. When the hour struck for flight there would be fewer eyes in the house, watching, speculating. Elizabeth could hardly wait for them to be gone. Aunt Hedley had arrived at a terrifyingly accurate conclusion the other night.

"You have arranged your plans more than you would have us believe," she remarked when Elizabeth evaded her final questions on the subject of a trip to Italy. "But you are right not to tell us—indeed I would rather not hear," she added hastily. "Only *don't be rash—that* is my only advice—" and with that, as if her unspoken thought had materialized him, Edward Barrett walked in. She spoke up quickly to cover her confusion.

"We were just observing, Edward, how much better Elizabeth is."

"Do you think so?" in a tone of complete disagreement.

"Do you pretend to say you see no surprising difference in her?"

Edward Barrett turned to look, and Elizabeth paled under his deliberate stare. He moved away with a shrug. "She doesn't talk."

"Perhaps she's nervous," offered Mrs. Hedley, speaking always with more truth than wisdom. Elizabeth bent her head over her needlework.

Her father seemed to have no more idea of her living beyond the four walls of her room "than of a journey to Lapland" Elizabeth wrote Browning, still, one couldn't be sure that some incident mightn't enlighten him. As if life in Wimpole Street was not tense enough already, Flush gave one last turn to the screw. He was stolen again—snatched off the streets as he followed Elizabeth into a shop.

Suspecting that Browning thought her unduly wrought up about Flush, Elizabeth defended both her anxiety and Flush's supine want of resistance. He must have been gagged, otherwise he would have bitten. On that point at least, Browning needed no convincing. Negotiations for her dog's return were being blocked by her brothers who objected to her paying a second large ransom, and by Edward Barrett who positively forbade it. Meanwhile the kidnappers were sending awful threats and Elizabeth grew frantic.

In the remote peace of his room in Hatcham, Browning read all about the commotion in Wimpole Street and thought it a great pity women were so easily terrorized. There was only one way to deal with thieves. What a comparison he could draw between submission to gangsters and submission to Edward Barrett! The chance was too good to be lost! He seized his pen.

But his tirade only provoked Elizabeth's goodnatured irony. Would he, she wanted to know, barter with the banditti in Italy, in case they absconded with her? And if they brought him one of her ears in proof of worse to come, would he still haggle over the price of getting her back? "It is as well to know beforehand perhaps," she laughed.

He had supposed Flush to be already safe at home or he would not have read her such a lecture at such a time, Browning half apologized; nevertheless the habit of yielding to tyranny was "lamentable weakness." "I can quite understand and allow for it in you—but weakness it essentially *is*, as you know perfectly," he insisted.

Weakness it is, Elizabeth agreed amiably. That point settled, she ordered a cab and with the panic-stricken and useless Wilson beside her, drove to the sordid area where the thieves had their hideout. Even a man thought twice of penetrating the London slums in those days. Her trip paved the way for Flush's quick return, on payment of an outrageous ransom, of course. In defiance of an entire male coalition against her, she got her dog back.

This proof of stamina Elizabeth laid triumphantly before her lover. He, meanwhile, for the first and almost the only time in his robust existence, had been ordered to bed by his doctor and placed on a diet of milk, "to correct the superabundant gall of bitterness which overflowed recently about Flush," Browning suggested humorously.

He was completely recovered fortunately, on Wednesday, September 10th, when an urgent message arrived from Elizabeth. Edward Barrett had moved with the suddenness of which she had warned. The Barrett family were to leave London. He had decided to renovate the Wimpole Street house from attic to cellar. Her brothers were even now hunting temporary quarters for them all outside the city.

"If we are taken away Monday, what then?" Elizabeth asked. "You must think for us both." And at the end of her somewhat distraught letter she gave the terse promise: "I will do as you wish—understand."

Browning replied without a moment's hesitation. "We must be *married directly* and go to Italy. I will go for a license today and we can be married on Saturday. I will call at three and arrange everything with you." Then careful to the very end not to exert pressure, he added: "It seems as if I should insult you if I spoke a word to confirm you, to beseech you, to relieve you from your promise, if you claim it."

"I was yours long ago," answered Elizabeth, "though you give me my promise back at this eleventh hour. So take it again for my sake and not your own."

⋘ Chapter Eighteen

. . . What I do
And what I dream include thee, as the
   wine
Must taste of its own grapes.
                SONNETS FROM THE PORTUGUESE

AT ELEVEN O'CLOCK on the morning of September 12th, Wilson and her mistress walked down Wimpole Street as rapidly as was possible for Elizabeth. Her legs felt weighted with lead, like those of a person in a nightmare who cannot run. A sickening fear obsessed her. Had Edward Barrett suspected all along? Was it for this he maneuvered them out of London? So strong was her sense of being pursued that in front of a chemist shop she nearly collapsed.

"In here Wilson—quick!"

The restorative bought at the chemist's steadied her and they started off again. At last Wilson was able to hail a cab and they climbed shakily into its concealing depths. Thanking a merciful heaven they were off the sidewalks, Wilson mopped her own brow as well as her mistress's with sal volatil.

St. Marylebone Church was not very distant. They reached it in ten minutes. Heavy, nail-studded doors swung open to their touch and shut solidly behind them. The high-vaulted gloom was cold, oppressive, and empty. Elizabeth held her breath, searching the dark and the silence. A step echoed suddenly and boldly on the stone flagging, a strong, warm hand closed over her chilled one.

"Robert!"

Half an hour later Elizabeth entered the house of Hugh Boyd alone. It was only a few doors from the church. A servant showed her into her old friend's library. The master was occupied, but would be down soon. Grateful to be quite alone Elizabeth sank into a chair. She had been married exactly fifteen minutes.

"It has been a great privilege, Mrs. Browning." The minister had shaken hands with her after the ceremony. "Mrs. Browning—Mrs. Robert Browning—" The thought was still incredible. Her mind faltered away from it to Elizabeth Barrett, standing in the dim glow of altar candles. She had been dimly aware of a stranger in the shadows near Robert. He was a Browning cousin, their second witness, it was explained. By her own side stood faithful Wilson in her somber maid's black—the only friend at her wedding!

The marriage rite had seemed furtive—its phrases

murmured like something forbidden, until Browning spoke out, shattering the illusion with his forthright "I, Robert, take thee Elizabeth—"

After that she remembered only the rapt look in his eyes, and how it bathed her in tenderness—protection—safety.

Hugh Boyd's shuffling step, the tap of his cane, recalled her to the present. She saw the blind man hesitate on the threshold, his hands extended.

"Elizabeth—there—I'm glad mine is the first blessing! You and I will drink to your happiness—and Robert Browning's. Here is bread and butter, too. You must eat," he commanded, "and pull yourself together before Henrietta and Arabel come." He chatted on with kindly tact because she did not speak.

Elizabeth had always been dear to Boyd. It was a comfort in old age to be her confidant—to fill the place of that father he disliked—who was a father only in name. Elizabeth's visit this morning had been prearranged. It was a convenient screen to hide what took place earlier in St. Marylebone Church.

"We were frightened—" Henrietta said accusingly, as soon as she arrived. "Really, Ba, no one goes calling at this hour of the day! You left no word with the maids—"

"And Flush—shut up in your room and whimpering—" interrupted Arabel.

"But I told you—I told you last night I was coming to see Mr. Boyd this morning," Elizabeth reminded them, "and you agreed to meet me here and drive with me afterwards to Hampstead Heath."

"We thought you meant this *afternoon.*"

How their eyes searched her face. How well they knew she concealed something!

"Well—but here we are," stammered Elizabeth, "and I'm afraid I've exhausted poor Mr. Boyd. We'd better be on our way."

They asked no more questions, but when the cab passed St. Marylebone Church Elizabeth kept her face well averted till the sudden rush of happiness that flooded her heart had subsided.

"I am all gratitude—and all pride . . . that my life has been so crowned by you." Robert Browning's elation overflowed in the letter he wrote as soon as he reached Hatcham. There had been no time for confidences. They had separated almost immediately after the ceremony. Elizabeth wrote also. She had constantly to wrench herself back to the realities of Wimpole Street lest the family notice her rapt silences.

She was in hourly uncertainty of Edward Barrett's next move. Under the circumstances she thought it wiser for Browning not to come again to the house, especially now they were married. Robert agreed thankfully. He had hated the thought of entering his wife's home in the guise of a friend. In a very few days now all the subterfuge—the hateful game of deception, could be dropped.

A house for the Barretts had not yet been found and they had a breathing space to complete their plans. Letters must be written, to be sent as soon as they left. In careful wording the secrecy of their marriage had to be explained to relatives and friends. Elizabeth proposed omitting the date from their wedding announcements; otherwise, she told Browning, she would be in a difficult position. She was still receiving callers as though she were Miss Barrett.

They had barely settled the matter of their announcements when word came that a house had been found in Bookham. The Barretts were leaving Wimpole Street Monday—it was then Thursday. There was no time to lose. Browning rushed to the city to consult train schedules.

His last-minute arrangements had to be transmitted to Elizabeth by post. She in turn was plying him with letters full of needful but distracting questions. Where must she meet him Saturday—the day set for flight? At what hour? She and Wilson were taking only the most necessary luggage—a very small amount. Still, it must be sent in advance, as they could not carry it out of the house unobserved. Should she dispatch her boxes in her name, or his? How much time must she allow to get from Wimpole Street to their meeting place?

In the pressure and excitement, feeling now the full weight of his responsibility for what they were doing, Browning got hopelessly mired in timetables. He made three blunders in the directions he sent, and Elizabeth, always alert and clear-headed in emergencies, detected each.

On September 19th their correspondence came to an end. Browning's last note was brief. He corrected his latest mistake and gave accurate final instructions. Then, aware of the anguish of her last hours under her father's roof, he reached out a comforting hand.

"God bless and strengthen you . . . write me one word more. Depend on me."

In Elizabeth's one word more is seen her knowledge that the bridge she burned would never be rebuilt. "By tomorrow at this time, I shall have *you* only to love me —my beloved! You *only!* As if one said *God only.*"

Pulling on her gloves, Wilson looked competently about the room. "I haven't forgotten nothing—no, Miss. Your umbrella, your rug, the small carpet-bag. They're all in the back entry where I put them while Cook and the others was eating breakfast. Everyone's too busy now to notice I'm leaving. In fifteen minutes I'll be waiting outside with a cab." She was careful to close the door noiselessly.

They were alone, Flush and his mistress. The room was deathly still except for the clock on the mantelpiece. Its ticking seemed to have grown much louder after Wilson went.

Elizabeth was cloaked and bonneted. Up and down and back and forth she paced, stopping occasionally to touch some object. She would never see anything in this room again. A single letter addressed to George Barrett lay on her desk. She had tried to write her father but had torn up each attempt. The picture of his anger was too indelible. When he stood over Henrietta that day years ago, as she lay at his feet, his face had been a mask of hate—repellent, livid with controlled rage.

The walk around her room began again. Her books— they had kept her from going mad, they were her friends. Would they be sent to her? Or would he destroy every trace of her presence in the house? The bust of Plato over the door looked down at her implacably. It had been his gift when she was twelve. She smoothed the crocheted throw folded neatly across the back of her chair. Her mother's handiwork had warmed and comforted her all these years!

The clock on the mantel chimed the half hour. Elizabeth bent swiftly over Flush, gathering him into her arms.

"Now," she whispered.

At the head of the stairs she stopped to listen. From below came the soft clink of china, the murmur of talk. Sette laughed out, Edward Barrett raised his dry voice. Lunch was being served late, as always on Saturdays, to accommodate the men of the family. She had chosen this moment. They would all be in one room—preoccupied.

Elizabeth leaned her body against the stair rail for support as she came down slowly, holding Flush. One hand was ready to close on his muzzle.

"Flush—" she breathed— "if you bark we are lost!"

He flattened himself against her breast.

The door of 50 Wimpole Street opened, then shut with a faint thud unheard in the Barrett dining-room. Hoofs rang on the paved street, accelerated to a brisk trot and died away. The sound was barely distinguishable in the silence hanging over the table. Lunch was over.

Edward Barrett laid aside his napkin and pushed back his chair. It was his invariable signal that the family could disperse. He himself retired on Saturdays to

his study in the rear of the house on the second floor.
There, behind a cloud of smoke from the best Jamaican
tobacco, he could study the market trends in the London news in undisturbed quiet.

On the second floor he came to Elizabeth's door.
Shut, as usual. She was probably lying about, reading or
scribbling. The indolent existence of an invalid suited
her temperament. The doctors pampered her—friends
lightened her solitude—that fellow Browning! He'd
found on coming home three weeks ago that she'd been
closeted with him all afternoon. When he demanded an
explanation it came glibly enough. A succession of thun-
derstorms had prevented his leaving. Well—the poet
hadn't been around recently; from which he concluded
that Elizabeth had noticed his displeasure. She had not
dared defy him in the Pisa matter. The incident, in fact,
had produced a change for the better. She had always
been opinionated, the result of giving her so much education and attention in childhood. Now she seemed
much less forward in her talk, waited for him to choose
a topic of conversation, and murmured "Yes, Papa" or
"No doubt, Papa." Her old habit of argument and discussion had been dropped—and so had the subject of
travel.

He had done well to make it so clear that anyone dis-
puting his authority was the loser. With the unhurried
tread of majestic complacency Edward Barrett walked
past Elizabeth's door to his study.

Some hours later Henrietta entered Elizabeth's room
and made the discovery which was to rock the household at 50 Wimpole Street. One can only hope she de-

rived some satisfaction from being the bearer of such unbelievable tidings to Edward Barrett. Dodging the book aimed at her head, she ran stumbling back to her room. Meanwhile Edward Barrett sought other ways to relieve his feelings. Wilson, he found, could not be turned into the street with her chances of future employment ruined. Even Flush was beyond his vindictive reach. But Arabel—Arabel had shared Elizabeth's room and must have known all along. She would pay for her silence.

Protests of innocence availed Arabel nothing. When the family returned from Bookham she was assigned a small, dark room, close to the servants' quarters. It was fireless in winter and airless in summer. She was reinstated only years later, when Henrietta herself escaped, and, as the remaining daughter, Arabel had to run her father's house and assume a position of dignity.

London newspapers announced the Browning marriage next day. The news took the world by surprise and Mr. Barrett met its surprise with impeccable Victorian dignity. Enquirers were told that his daughter was a hopeless invalid. In his opinion she should have been preparing herself to meet her Creator, instead of which she had indulged her romantic notions and run off with a poet! He raised his hands in a pious gesture of resignation.

Elizabeth's brothers were righteously indignant. It was regrettable that Browning had not dealt openly with the men of the family. The affair had been clandestine. Not the sort of behavior expected from a gentleman.

They had everything to gain by upholding their father. The temptation must have been irresistible, for Browning himself knew he had been placed in an indefensible position. Moreover they were men, at a period and in a country where women of the family were helpless dependents. That a sister as weak and incapable of action as Elizabeth had deceived them—outmaneuvered them all, irked their pride.

Henrietta and Arabel, who were more completely at their father's mercy than anyone else, were the only ones to behave with gallantry. They sent letters to Elizabeth immediately to cheer and hearten her—to assure her of their continued love and loyalty.

◆§ *Chapter Nineteen*

A place to stand and love in for a day . . .
SONNETS FROM THE PORTUGUESE

AS THE DOOR of Wimpole Street shut for good, Elizabeth felt a moment's crushing sense of the fatality of her step. All of the past that had been sweet reached out its clinging tentacles. All she could see ahead was a still unwritten page. There had been a kind of safety in the joyless years behind her, because there had been nothing to lose. Now everything was at stake. The future hung precariously on what Robert Browning imagined her to be.

"You make me uneasy often," she had protested barely a month ago, "through this extravagance of over-estimation; forcing me to contract 'obligations to pay' which I look at in speechless despair." Again and again she sought to bring the poet down to realities. "Promise me not to say to your family any foolishness about me—remember what the recoil will be, and understand that I must suffer in proportion to all the over-praises." Only recently he had spoken disparagingly of another woman whom he had compared to Elizabeth. "No wonder that your father should give you books of logic to study," she remonstrated, "if you do not understand that I am no better than she, except by your loving me better; that the cause is not in her or me, but in you only."

The conviction that she must fail him was never stronger than at this final turn in the road. Long since, she had vowed to leave Browning if she saw that he wearied of their marriage. This resolution was all she had to cling to now, as she passed down Wimpole Street to meet the coming years.

While hope still faltered the cab slowed and came to a stop in front of Hodgson's, the London bookshop where Browning waited. In his enveloping greatcoat and soft brimmed hat he looked unfamiliar. The Browning she knew, dressed for the drawing-room, had been a meticulously groomed—almost dapper figure. The rough homespun of his ulster, its look of sturdy durability, brought out all his own enduring qualities. Elizabeth leaned forward, forgetting the poet, seeing for the first time the man alone—staunch, true, dependable.

He stepped in beside her and without a word gathered her into his arms. That silent embrace, tender, possessive, and close, dissolved all her doubts. Browning took from her the gold wedding ring, worn all the past week inside her dress. It was still warm. He kissed it and placed it gently on her finger.

"My love—my wife," whispered Robert. His steady gaze, ardent and compelling, drew nearer. Slowly he laid his lips on hers.

Wilson, seated outside with the cab driver, minded her own business with Sphinx-like detachment. All during the rail trip to the coast and the channel crossing she remained obligingly deaf, dumb, and blind, like the perfect, inscrutable English servant she was. The lovers felt themselves blissfully isolated and alone. Determined to keep Elizabeth's thoughts off what was happening at home, Browning succeeded in making present happiness a great deal more real than any imagined violence transpiring in Wimpole Street.

Flush behaved perfectly on this lap of the journey, stunned, no doubt, by his liberation from four walls into a bewildering world. His protests came later when he was shut up in a crate by the "barbarians" in charge of continental trains.

Once arrived in Paris, Browning insisted on stopping for a few days. He was careful not to push Elizabeth beyond her strength, and after the tension of the past months they both needed a rest. In Paris they encountered Mrs. Jameson, the friend who had wanted to escort Elizabeth to Pisa. She too was on her way to Italy, with a niece, and to Browning's immense relief she agreed to join them, traveling by slow stages to Marseille, from whence they would all embark for Genoa.

The trip was no carefree honeymoon to Browning,

who knew that his wife would never complain of the
pace he set, and that he must guess the extent of her
frailty. The presence of an older woman, and one who
had more knowledge and authority than Wilson, was a
support to him.

They were still in France when the first packet of letters from England caught up with them. Elizabeth shut
Browning firmly out of her room and opened her mail
alone. Her preference for facing such ordeals by herself
was not to be altered. The harsh letter from her father
was the last message she was ever to receive from him.
It is likely that she destroyed it without showing it to
Browning. She had anticipated its cruelty. It was
George's answer to her plea for understanding which
hurt her most. He had been a sympathetic fellow suf-
ferer while she was home—what made him reverse himself? Fortunately in the same mail there were affectionate messages from Henrietta, Arabel, and John Kenyon.

Pisa, the Brownings' destination, was reached about
a month later. To Elizabeth, who had looked at the four
walls of her room for seven years, the novelty of travel—
the sudden liberation into a world of great scenic beauty
was an indescribable experience—a kind of rebirth. The
impact of so many new and vivid impressions and the
adjustment to undreamed-of personal happiness had
been emotionally taxing. She was thankful to settle
down at last in the three rooms overlooking the famous
leaning tower of Pisa which Robert found for them.

In her relation to Browning she knew at last a great
security. The proof that mere words can never give, that
she could only gain through intimate association, was

now hers. Ten days after their flight she had been able to write Henrietta: "I feel to have the power to make him happy—I feel to have it in my hands. It is strange that anyone so brilliant should love *me*—but true and strange it is—and it is impossible for me to doubt it any more."

Eager that other people's approval of her marriage reach her family and come indirectly to her father's ears, she told her sisters how Mrs. Jameson had declared that no two people anywhere on earth were more obviously made for each other. Mrs. Jameson, her niece and Wilson had all three lost their hearts to Robert. He was the perfect traveling companion, thought constantly of other people's wants and was himself never tired or ill-humored.

As for his goodness to herself, it was beyond anything she had imagined. "We love each other," Elizabeth wrote, "with a love that grows instead of diminishing. I speak to you of such things rather than of the cathedral at Bourges, because it is of these, I feel sure, that you desire knowledge rather."

It was indeed! Henrietta and Arabel, starved for whatever crumbs of romance she could throw their way, were not remotely interested in the cathedral at Bourges!

The Brownings spent the next six months in close companionship by their own fireside. Winter came to Pisa as well as to other places, although it was blessed with more sunshine than England, and warmth and quiet were essential to Elizabeth. Far from missing his wide circle of friends in London, the convivial Browning flew into a panic now whenever public interest awakened by their romance threatened their privacy. Already English acquaintances had written to say their travels would bring them close to Pisa. With or without the slightest encouragement they would call on the Brownings—the implication was plain!

"Those people will spoil all our happiness, if we once let them in—you will see—if you speak of your health and save yourself on that plea, they will seize upon *me!*" Browning paced the floor excitedly.

Secretly delighted that he showed no impatience yet for outside diversion, Elizabeth laughed at him. *She* was not going to let anyone in, she insisted.

"There is that coarse, vulgar Mrs. T——," Robert continued, as if the offenders were already at the door. "I do hope, Ba, if you don't wish to give me the greatest pain, that you won't receive that vulgar pushing woman who is not fit to speak to you."

It was immensely gratifying to be able to repeat all this to Henrietta—to show that Robert was perfectly satisfied for the present to let life remain a prolonged tête-à-tête. The two of them had, in truth, not nearly exhausted the novelty of being together day after day instead of an hour a week. They discussed avidly every topic under the sun, talked, as most lovers do, a great deal of nonsense, laughed like children and cared not a fig what Wilson might think.

Bereft of books they had been forced to leave behind, they subscribed for eightpence a month to the local library in Pisa and yawned over Italian fiction until Elizabeth, ignoring Robert's protests, sent to Paris for

French novels and observed, to her great satisfaction, that he was as much entertained by "wickedness" as she!

Flush, completely won over to marital life, stretched himself luxuriously before the flames at their feet, accompanied Browning on long walks, and picked up bad habits and not a few fleas from disreputable canine acquaintances met on these rambles. He had come a long way from the lap-dog servitude of Wimpole Street. It was *he* now, who decided when Browning needed a walk and barked till he got his way.

They had been in Pisa a full month before Elizabeth summoned enough courage to show her husband the sequence of love sonnets on which she had been at work the better part of two years. As he stood one morning at a window alone, she stole quietly into the room. Placing one hand on his shoulder to prevent his turning, she thrust the sheaf of papers into his hand.

"They are yours," she said in a low voice. "Tear them up if you don't like them."

Reading the intimate and moving record of her love, Robert Browning knew they belonged to the world rather than himself. They were the highest poetic expression she had yet achieved. It was he who proposed the title, *Sonnets from the Portuguese,* to give them anonymity and because the word "Portuguese" suggested a poem of Elizabeth's he specially loved and identified with her. Browning pronounced the poems the greatest sonnet sequence since Shakespeare. They were indeed unique in her day and will always remain an undying contribution to English poetry.

The weeks in Pisa passed in serenity and great happiness. Elizabeth's peace of mind was augmented by the discovery that they could live in Italy for almost nothing. For from the moment she had received her father's letter, she knew they were in financial difficulties. Edward Barrett had written that he would neither forward her income nor manage her investments. He wished her to know that from now on she had ceased to exist—as far as he was concerned.

Happily for them, John Kenyon came to their rescue before the sum borrowed from Browning's father had been exhausted. He had refused to get himself involved in the affairs of his Barrett cousins up to this moment. But now he went indignantly to Wimpole Street and assumed full management of Elizabeth's finances. In March he sent her the income her father had withheld, explaining to her the steps he had taken to ensure her receiving what was hers, and insisting that Robert and she call upon him for added funds should they find their means insufficient.

It was a kindness she and Robert never forgot and never availed themselves of. Browning had a horror of debt. Elizabeth found that her husband could teach her many practical economies—a lesson that a daughter of a wealthy West Indian planter had never had to learn. Modest as their income and earnings were, they were enough to live on frugally yet comfortably, in Italy, and they were both satisfied with little.

In April, the Brownings left for Florence. Their stay in Pisa had been spent in a seclusion as quiet and unbroken as that of Wimpole Street. Now Elizabeth emerged into the sunlight of the Florentine city, into such gayety and charm as she did not know existed.

From their rooms overlooking the Via delle Belle Donne she watched the colorful street life of the town. In Italy poverty seemed not to go hand in hand with misery. Here the poor sang, and laughed. Florence was a city of enchanting contrasts. The bright cotton umbrellas of street markets sprouted like mushrooms under the walls of ancient palaces, the Duomo's immense dome rose above narrow streets, and a stone's throw from Giotto's graceful tower flowed the mud-colored Arno, under the shabby, tilted houses of the Ponte Vecchio. From the moment she set foot in Florence, Elizabeth gave her heart to Italy.

◄§ *Chapter Twenty*

. . . *God's gifts put man's best dreams
to shame.*
SONNETS FROM THE PORTUGUESE

THE ITALIAN SUMMER arrived early and seemed somewhat overpowering to two people used to the cool temperatures of England. They were glad to escape from it on a brief trip into the high, forested mountains of Vallombroso, Robert traveling on horse-back up the steep slopes while Elizabeth and Wilson rode in basket sledges drawn by white oxen. Winding their slow way among the "ink-black" pines, drinking in each lovelier view as the trail dipped now into a ravine or climbed still higher, the journey seemed a primitive breath-catching adventure to the Wimpole Street pris-oner of a few months ago.

Back once more in Florence, they settled down to endure the heat philosophically. A piano had been rented for Robert, the galleries, filled with priceless art treasures, were close at hand, to be enjoyed in company with a husband who had himself the knowledge and perceptions of an artist. Their delight in each other's companionship never palled, although "being too happy doesn't agree with literary activity quite as well as I should have thought," Elizabeth confessed to her old friend Miss Mitford.

She had never really been happy in her life before, she informed Henrietta, who was at this time needing encouragement to take a matrimonial risk of her own. She and Robert never quarreled, asserted Elizabeth. He was so persistently devoted, in fact, that she was beginning to wonder if she was not, after all, the angel he imagined her!

"It is not so bad a thing, be sure, for a woman to be loved by a man of imagination," wrote the wife, who, but a short time ago, had feared precisely that.

The whole Browning ménage was falling under the spell of romance. Wilson was receiving marked attentions from a picturesque member of the Grand Duke's bodyguard, and Flush, roaming the streets of Florence without danger from kidnappers, had amorous adventures of his own.

"Disgraceful behavior—for a respectable dog like you," Browning reproved him one morning when he returned at dawn wearing a comic expression of guilt. Flush slunk into the kitchen and after drinking up an enormous bowl of water, judiciously made himself as inconspicuous as possible for the rest of the day.

With the coming of autumn the two exiles had no

thought of leaving the city they had grown to think of as home, but they did move to larger rooms in the Piazza Pitti. Here they celebrated their first wedding anniversary. The year had been rich in emotional adventure. They had explored undiscovered territory in each other and found immense rewards. As long as life lasted they were to penetrate these regions of companionship, finding streams that would never run dry, paths that would never look familiar.

Their self-sufficiency was a necessary precaution as well as a preference. The provincial dullness of English compatriots abroad was proverbial. Gradually, however, they found congenial spirits among the sculptors, painters, and writers drawn to Florence for obvious reasons. Isa Blagden, an English writer, was one of these. She became the intimate friend of their married years. Through her they were in touch with the most interesting of the foreign colony. Miss Blagden's villa at Bellosguardo was a gathering place for the Tennysons, the Thackerays, Margaret Fuller Ossoli, Bulwer Lytton, the Hawthornes, and many other people of note and of various nationalities, living in Florence for a time or merely passing through.

By the following spring Elizabeth and Browning were both tired of meals carried to their rooms, continental style, from a near-by restaurant. They were ready, after their prolonged honeymoon, to become householders. An apartment was found in the one-time palace of the Conte Guidi. It was spacious, and the terrace on which its living rooms opened offered cooling air and perfect seclusion from the street. It became their

permanent home. They plunged now into the fun and
exasperations of furnishing it. Florentine auction sales
and the low prices of dealers were irresistibly tempting.
Elizabeth had one left-over obsession from years of invalidism. There must be plenty of sofas. Browning had
a devotion to bureaus. Appalled finally by the influx of
these commodities, they called a halt, but not before
Elizabeth had acquired eight sofas and Browning six
dressers!

In time they covered the bare walls of Casa Guidi
with faded brocades and rare old primitives overlooked
by wealthier collectors. Books, finally sent from England, filled their living-room shelves. Antiques were
easy to procure in Florence, most of them for a song.
The gleam of old brass and the mellow note of Italian
pottery enriched Casa Guidi and provided a colorful
background for two poets.

The interest of Florentine society in the Brownings
was lasting, not only by virtue of their achievements,
but because each was a striking personality. Browning's immense vitality, the wide range of his talents, his
provocative ideas, and his hearty enthusiasms seemed to
fill Casa Guidi, until one became aware of Elizabeth—
very small, quietly alert, with a burning intensity smol-
dering behind her dark eyes. She let her husband dominate the conversation, but she held everyone's attention
effortlessly when she chose.

The joyous emotions of that first year and a half of
marriage had overpowered creative impulses, but now
their hearts had quieted. Happiness was no longer something ecstatic and impermanent, to be caught on the

wing and tasted while it lasted. Out of their deep certainty of each other the desire to write began to stir once more. Stimulated by what she was witnessing in Florence of the *risorgimento*, the birth of Italian nationalism, Elizabeth began a long political poem called *Casa Guidi Windows*.

Italy at that time was still divided into small kingdoms and duchies, the private domains of Austrian princes who were virtually dictators. Piedmont alone was ruled by an Italian and from this province stemmed the present movement for a free and unified nation.

Just previous to the Brownings' arrival in Italy, Pope Pius IX, a man of liberal policies, had initiated democratic reforms in the Papal State. This move alarmed Metternich, rightly interpreting the spread of democratic ideas in Italy as a threat to Austrian rule. He sent his troops across the border to quell any incipient revolution and precipitated the first clash with forces working for a federated Italy.

From her home in Casa Guidi Elizabeth was to watch the long and painful growth of freedom in the Italian consciousness. She learned to mistrust the highly volatile emotions of the populace, vacillating between loyalty to their old feudal masters and the new idea of patriotism, and she was often bitterly disillusioned by the equal vacillation and treachery of Italy's liberal leaders.

Whether or not she saw in all this a parallel to her own struggle for independence, it was her intimate knowledge of the horrors of Negro slavery and her personal experience of tyranny that gave her such passionate interest in the liberation of all who were subjugated.

Most of her poetry from now on was written to further the idea of emancipation in one form or another. Her ballad, "The Runaway Slave at Pilgrim's Point," the story of a slave who strangles her child born of a white master, was written to aid the abolitionist movement in America. "A Curse for a Nation," a fiery indictment of American tolerance of Negro slavery, created a great stir and made her temporarily unpopular. Her longest and most ambitious piece of work, *Aurora Leigh,* was basically a plea for the emancipation of women; and her purpose in writing *Casa Guidi Windows* was to try and enlist English sympathy for Italy's fight against Austrian domination.

Marriage with a man like Robert Browning encouraged crusading. He too had a West Indian background and a detestation of human slavery in all its manifestations. He wanted no docile wife. His fierce insistence that Elizabeth be herself with a mind and will of her own was very different from the conjugal submission stamped on her memory from Hope End days.

"Don't say such words to me!" Browning cried out in the first months of marriage, when Elizabeth gave in eagerly to his wishes and preferences.

"Why—what ought I to say then?" Was ever a husband so unlike husbands in general!

"Say that you will do as you please as long as you please to do it." And so Elizabeth obeyed. Amused and grateful, she recovered some of her childhood's spirited independence.

Her interest in foreign politics was already beginning to clash with the insular views of her British friends. In close touch with the new democratic ideas that were fomenting revolutions on the continent, she was fast becoming a citizen of the world. She could not have escaped these influences if she had wanted to. Italy was awakening out of centuries-old lethargy. In France the unpopular Second Empire was heading the country toward a rebirth of republican ideals. Various brands of socialism were the newest topic of the day. Marx and Engels had recently published their *Manifest Der Kommunisten,* a pamphlet widely read and distributed. The Brownings were in sympathy with socialistic trends. Elizabeth especially was increasingly out of sympathy with the imperialism of her own country. Alarmed and alienated, some of her English friends wondered if she was becoming a Communist. However, she answered this question very clearly in a letter to John Kenyon:

"Nothing can be more hateful to me than this communist idea of quenching individualities in the mass. As if the hope of the world did not always consist in the eliciting of the individual man from the background of the masses, in the evolvement of individual genius, virtue, magnanimity."

Elizabeth the poet had immediately detected the threat to individual creative expression underlying Communism.

In the month of March, 1849, a son, Robert Wiedeman Barrett Browning was born to the Brownings. Childbirth had not been forbidden Elizabeth by her doctors. Medical opinion in general regarded pregnancy and birth as natural functions, beneficial even to a woman in delicate health, provided she had no organic difficulties. For some time his parents called the baby Wiedeman, that being the maiden name of Browning's mother, but as soon as the little boy could talk he referred to himself as "Penini," a nickname which clung to him.

Robert's jubilant relief that his wife had come through her ordeal safely was eclipsed two days later by the news of his mother's death. The plunge from joy to grief was sudden—a shock from which he did not soon recover. The drama of Elizabeth's home life had been such a major concern that Browning had never stressed his own family problems. He had left England not knowing when he would return at a time when his mother's health was failing. Between them there had been unusually close ties of understanding affection. Remorse that he had let her die without the comfort of seeing him once more preyed on him.

Frequently now when Elizabeth entered a room where he sat alone, she found him in tears. Meantime, Elizabeth hid her own pain that a letter to her father, announcing the birth of his grandson, remained unanswered. Foolishly, incorrigibly, she had hoped the news might soften him.

In July, Elizabeth being strong enough to travel, they went to the mountain resort of Bagni di Lucca for a month, as much to lift Robert out of despondency as to escape the heat of Florence. John Kenyon's generosity made the excursion possible. On hearing of the birth of their child he had immediately forwarded one hundred pounds. From now on this sum became his annual gift and was gratefully used for summer vacations.

Browning had been slower than Elizabeth in getting back to his writing. Disinclination for creative labor since his mother's death had been difficult to surmount; however, her passing had revived in him an old inward struggle to reconcile the orthodox faith in which she had reared him with his present undenominational beliefs. He now began work on "Christmas Eve and Easter Day," an endeavor to define Christianity in terms that would admit all faith and creeds. But Browning himself was still groping. Much of what he wrote was in his old, obscure manner, a fact which did not escape his critics, while what he said clearly offended orthodox readers.

Browning and Elizabeth were always to say what they had to say and let the chips fall where they might. At odds with class privilege, selfish nationalism, and insular pride, their plain speaking (especially Elizabeth's, because she wrote of contemporary issues), was made at the expense of popularity and literary prestige.

Elizabeth had no illusions about the probable reception in her own country of her poem *Casa Guidi Windows*. It was published while England was in the full stride of empire building, when the birth pangs of a small Latin nation were of little moment to the British. "I have a book coming out in England called *Casa Guidi Windows*," she wrote her friend Isa Blagden, "which will prevent everybody else (except you) from speaking to me again."

Meanwhile their month's stay in Bagni di Lucca fortified them both, in spirit and body. Browning regained
some of his serenity tramping the blue hills of the Tuscan countryside and Elizabeth was able for the first
time to accompany him on short rambles. The baby
thrived in the crisp mountain air. He was quite small,
but rosy, cheerful, and healthy. He had blue eyes, gold
curls, and "a beaming thinking little face" as his mother
proudly described it.

On their return to Florence from Bagni di Lucca, the
Brownings were compelled for a while to live in a state
of siege within Casa Guidi. The Grand Duke of Tus-
cany had played traitor to the cause of Italian freedom
and opened his gates to the entry of Metternich's troops.
There was little resistance but it was wiser for foreigners
to remain out of sight.

Watching the dust-covered gun carriages of the Aus-
trians roll unchallenged under her windows, Elizabeth
felt the betrayal of Italian leaders as keenly as if this
had been her own country. The only light touch in the
depressing picture was the innocent delight of Penini
and Flush in the commotion, the hard tramp of marching feet, the shouts, and the bugle calls. "I am afraid he
even admires the Austrian uniform," his mother said ruefully of Penini.

Wilson was suffering disillusionment with Italians,
too. The handsome member of the Civic Guard to whom
she had been engaged abandoned his suit with as little
conscience as his ducal master had deserted the Italian
cause. Fortunately Wilson was British and sensible, and
there was always Alessandro, the new servant, to exas-

perate her so that she forgot her melancholy. He talked incessantly about his prowess as a cook, resented her interference in the kitchen, and frankly expressed his dim opinion of the "Inglesi." On one matter only they agreed. The Signor was an angel—and ah, yes, the Signora too.

"I have seen many women," Alessandro announced, describing a wide arc with his soup ladle to indicate the extent of his knowledge, "I have been to Paris—I have been to Germany—I have been to London—and I have never known a Signora to spend so few scudi on her apparel. And then the Signor—how extraordinary for a Signor to be always sitting with his wife! And an English Signor too—why London is the most immoral city in the world—" at which point Wilson turned crimson, slammed the door in his face and retreated to her own quarters.

In peaceful contrast to the friction belowstairs, Robert and Elizabeth played in the living-room with their baby. Now that Penini took an interest in toys, Browning was capable of spending an idle hour or two practicing the art of spinning a top to amuse his son. Although mild disagreement had begun between Robert and Elizabeth over the rearing of Penini, it usually ended in laughter over Robert's inconsistencies—or her own! They were no different from most parents with an only child on whom too much attention is lavished.

It was during the spring of this year that Elizabeth received news of Henrietta's marriage to her guardsman of the resplendent scarlet uniforms—Mr. Surtees Cook. As was to be expected, Edward Barrett cast off his second daughter as he had Elizabeth. Arabel remained the only woman at 50 Wimpole Street, and refused her sisters' offers of a home with them. She stayed dutifully under her father's roof till he died, gentle and submissive always, and making for herself, it is to be hoped, a kind of life outside the reach of his interference.

Since her escape Elizabeth had not been troubled by unhappy reports of events in Wimpole Street. The second crisis over Henrietta's affair revived memories that would never lose their power to disturb and hurt. As the enervating heat of another summer descended on Florence, Elizabeth seemed unable to meet it with the same buoyancy of spirit. She tired so easily that Browning began to worry.

"Take her to the mountains," ordered the Italian doctor. Accordingly, they left for Siena. The cool air there and the change of environment obliterated morbid memories and physical weakness so successfully that on their return to Florence Elizabeth had one of her rare periods of entirely normal living, walking out each day, busy with her writing and her household affairs. This, their fifth autumn in Italy, brought with it a great sense of well-being. Life had never seemed richer. Evenings alone by the fire were still cherished as the best. They hoped, often futilely, that no one would drop in to call. When left to themselves, Robert would settle himself gratefully in an easy chair before the flames, and Elizabeth, on a pillow at his feet, leaned against his knees, while twilight stained the windows of Casa Guidi a deep purple.

Penini trotted in for his good-night kiss, and when he

left, the burning logs snapped an accompaniment to Robert's voice reading aloud the newest book from England: *David Copperfield*. Flush laid his graying muzzle on the hot hearth and dozed fitfully, stupefied by the warmth and by the murmur of voices he loved.

✒ Chapter Twenty-One

I seek no copy now of life's first half:
Leave here the pages with long musing
* curled,*
And write me new my future's epi-
* graph . . . .*
                    SONNETS FROM THE PORTUGUESE

ELIZABETH HAD AT FIRST cherished the hope
that Henrietta and her husband might choose to
live near her on the continent where they could exist on
a very small income a great deal more cheaply and comfortably than in England. But to her sister and brother-
in-law genteel poverty in England was a thousand times
better than living among foreigners. Accused sometimes
of disloyalty to her own country because she had
found health and happiness in another, Elizabeth could
be caustic about the disadvantages of her native land.

"As to living in England," she wrote Henrietta, "your
patriotism will be a sublime thing if you and Surtees

should prefer doing so really . . . my private opinion is that England should be less dear, if we are to practice the virtue of living in her. In that case, it would only remain for us to get over the objection of her having the worst climate in the world."

It was not until the summer of 1851 that Elizabeth was to see Henrietta again, at which time Robert was willing for her to risk the long journey home. They left Florence in May of that year, heading for the north of Italy and making prolonged stops in Venice, Padua, Milan, and other art centers. The long trip through Switzerland and France was accomplished happily. Travel always amused Elizabeth, who delighted in the movement and change after so many years of confinement.

In Paris there was a memorable first meeting with Alfred Tennyson, who called on them as soon as he heard of their arrival and carried them off for tea at his own hotel. He had been reading Browning's poems all the previous evening to some friends, he said. With such a persuasive beginning real friendship developed. Elizabeth was delighted with a poet laureate discriminating enough to admire her husband's work.

Once in London, she experienced the long anticipated joy of seeing Arabel and Henrietta again and also the pain which seemed inevitable as soon as her life touched that of her father. Not only did Edward Barrett return to the Brownings' hotel, unopened, the letter she had sent him announcing their arrival and pleading for a reconciliation, but he returned also all the letters she had written him since her marriage in a persistent effort to end the estrangement.

Sick at heart, Elizabeth turned for comfort to a renewal of affection with her brothers, who had the grace to come and see her and meet their young nephew, Penini. The longed-for meeting with Browning's father and sister Sarianna took place at last, and established a warm and loving relation. On this visit to London Elizabeth found herself plunged into greater activity than she had ever known. She and Robert had business to transact with their publishers, and old friends overwhelmed them with invitations. Hugh Boyd had died two years previously, but the aged Treppy was as vivacious as ever, and John Kenyon, in high spirits over their return, rained hospitality on them.

By the end of September, however, cold, penetrating fogs drove them to Paris, where they found sunny winter quarters on the Avenue des Champs-Élysées. During the next six months the French capital offered them plenty of stimulation. Napoleon III suppressed an attempted coup d'état, thereby plunging the city into a mild revolution.

Wintering in Paris was a trial of strength Elizabeth had wanted to make for Robert's sake as well as for the advantage of remaining a little nearer to her sisters. In Paris Robert took those periodic excursions into painting and sculpture which puzzled some of his friends and which his wife defended. Out of such intimate knowledge of the arts some of his best poems were born.

Elizabeth was keeping her word not to be a burden, but the winter of 1852 was the severest France had known in many years. It caused a return of old chest difficulties, forcing her to remain indoors while Robert, satisfied that she preferred it that way, went out for them both.

It was during this stay in Paris that Elizabeth persuaded Browning to let her call on George Sand. Browning had strong objections to the sort of company surrounding Sand, but he yielded. A meeting was arranged with the woman whose emancipated views and powerful intellect had long fascinated Elizabeth. The two, when they came face to face, offered a striking contrast: one intensely vivid and feminine, her genius transcending frailty, the other heavy and thick-set, with nothing to indicate the imperious mind but her flashing eyes.

Impulsively Elizabeth raised the hand laid in hers to her lips.

"*Non!*" exclaimed Sand sharply. "*Je ne veux pas!*" and bending, she kissed her visitor on the mouth. A woman's admiration was rare. She did not conceal the fact that it touched her.

Robert endured the ordeal politely, managing to hide his distaste when he was introduced to her bevy of men satellites and admitting later that the serene scorn with which she treated them won his grudging respect.

"I did not love her," Elizabeth wrote afterwards, "but I felt the burning soul through all that quietness."

The Brownings delayed their return from Paris to London until the following July and then stayed only briefly. Elizabeth seemed to have no resistance to meet the approaching English autumn. Alarmed by her weakness and the cough which always sent him into a panic, Browning packed up their luggage and hurried his family south, back to the warmth blazing from Italian skies.

With a sigh of content the two settled again into the leisurely tempo of Florentine life. The sunny rooms of Casa Guidi seemed all at once the most secure haven they would ever find for happiness.

From Florence Elizabeth wrote Henrietta that the pleasures and excitements of their London sojourn seemed not to have agreed with her after so many years of seclusion. But there was a deeper cause. In England she had sunk into the quicksands of the past. Morbid memories of unhappiness and ill-health, the still broken relation with her father, her dread of the English climate, all had flooded back on her in an overwhelming tide. Nor had she realized until then what an immense distance she had traveled from her home environment. Her ideas and sympathies had changed greatly during her five years among genial Italians.

"Our poor English want educating in gladness," she once wrote, watching the uninhibited gayety of the Florentines, "they want refining not in the fire but in the sunshine."

However, once restored to the peace of Casa Guidi, Elizabeth shook off the depression and the physical ills contracted in England. All the interesting contacts she had made, the new ideas gained through a year and a half of travel, began to crystallize. She was hardly home before all these factors drove her into fresh creative effort.

With the exception of the *Sonnets from the Portuguese,* Elizabeth never put more of herself into any poem than she did into *Aurora Leigh,* a romantic novel in verse, embodying her deep convictions regarding the wrongs endured by women of her period.

It is a commentary on her day that she expected and did find readers for three hundred and fifty pages of blank verse; that John Ruskin pronounced *Aurora Leigh* "the finest poem written in any language this century," and that Swinburne admired it—a trifle less rapturously —as "one of the longest poems in the world without a single dead line." Today *Aurora Leigh* is scarcely remembered, much less read. Its protest against social evils startled Victorian England. It was branded unfit reading for young females, whereupon they read it avidly, in secret, and imbibed a number of advanced ideas.

The poem was written between interruptions—the familiar one of intermittent ill-health, the care and education of Penini, and increasing social demands. Visitors to Casa Guidi were much more frequent now. They found their hostess cheerfully willing to lay aside her work and receive them. The habit of spasmodic work had not changed since the days when arduous mental labor could not be long sustained.

While Elizabeth patiently added line upon line to *Aurora Leigh,* Robert labored on *Men and Women,* that series of soliloquies and portraits which was to establish him for all time as a poet of the first rank. For himself, Robert insisted on a retreat, a study where creative work was safe from the intrusion of a child's voice or the disturbances of a household.

The winter of 1853 passed happily thus and with

great rapidity, for Elizabeth was well, her work engrossing, and on their return from England the Brownings
had found several new residents in Florence who were
congenial. Chief among these was young Robert Lytton,
son of Bulwer Lytton, the novelist, and an attaché at
the English embassy in Florence.

Robert Lytton and Elizabeth soon discovered a common enthusiasm. Both were interested in spiritualism,
the new cult which had captured the imagination of
hundreds of adherents in England and America. For
Elizabeth the subject had an irresistible fascination,
heightened perhaps by unhealed grief over a dead
brother. Her invalid life, with its lack of normal diversions, was always to be a powerful factor in making
her an easy prey to her emotions. While she admitted
that séances gave unreliable evidence and that charla-
tans among spiritualists were numerous, she accepted a
great deal that Robert rejected as pure fraud. To her
great chagrin, his opinion that the whole thing was a
hoax could never be shaken.

Robert deplored his wife's absorption in what he
considered a morbid and fantastic piece of humbug, but
characteristically, he never questioned her right to in-
vestigate, nor was his affection for Robert Lytton in
the least affected by that young man's persistent bringing to Casa Guidi an influence he thought unhealthy
and fraudulent.

Spiritualism was a matter of deep and lasting disagreement between Elizabeth and Browning, but
whereas other people allow rancor to creep into their
differences, they never did. They were by this time in

frequent opposition too over Penini, over politics, and in their estimates of people. Yet they understood each other profoundly, making room for each other's divergences of temperament and respecting each other's right to independent thought and action.

"Do you and Surtees quarrel as Robert and I do, about keeping the nursery in decent shadow on social occasions?" Elizabeth asked Henrietta, adding in self-defense: "Nobody resists Penini in the house, if he once has a mind to insist on a thing—Robert as little as anybody."

At four and a half, Penini was so lonely for the companionship of other children that he begged his mother to have their man-servant "catch a little boy" for him. His need went to Elizabeth's heart. She tried to fill in the gap for him as much as possible by allowing him a share of the adult life at Casa Guidi. Penini's every gesture and much of his talk had become unconscious imitation of his parents. At three he exclaimed shrilly over scenic wonders and struck attitudes of rapt delight when he was shown architectural beauties. He called his mother "Ba" and his father "mine de-ar Robert." It would have taken sterner natures than either of them possessed not to enjoy this comedy. And just as he aped their mannerisms and speech, he took on their adult interests, showing a precocious aptitude for music and art, and begging at an early age to be taught to read.

Elizabeth thought her adoration of him harmless, but she was unconciously shaping him into a reflection of herself. Her horror of being an autocratic parent pushed her into too great leniency. Her invalidism made her pamper him physically and her feminine influence smothered all the healthy crudities natural to a small boy. As he grew older Penini was to protest against maternal impositions such as kid shoes and velvet suits, but he was too fond of her to rebel and not sufficiently with other boys to suffer acutely from teasing.

Browning saw what was happening, but could do little more than frankly disapprove. He must have considered more than once the only cure for the situation —to send Penini back to England for his education, as so many expatriated English people did, but the separation would have been cruel to Elizabeth. So drastic a step would most certainly have shaken her health, if not her tenuous hold on life. When Penini did go to school in England, after his mother's death, he was never able to adjust, either to the discipline, which was Spartan, or to the rough give and take of his schoolfellows. The promise of his childhood was thus never fulfilled. He grew into a dilettante, a charming but rather ineffectual man, who found the mental and physical climate of Italy more congenial than that of his own country. He remained an expatriate all his life.

However, at present, in his fifth summer, Penini was given an answer at last to his prayer for a playmate, in the small son of William Story, an American sculptor summering with his family at Bagni di Lucca, whither the Brownings had gone. Young Lytton joined the friendly party for a few weeks. Mornings were reserved for writing but afternoon and the lovely blue mountains drew everyone outdoors. Fortunately for Robert the presence of Story made it possible to divert conversation from spiritualism to lively discussions on art.

The natural sequence to such happy companionship was to follow the Storys to Rome. Robert had long wanted to winter there, and Elizabeth was well enough, eager for travel, and curious to meet the many people in Rome, who, William Story assured her, were communicating successfully with the spirit world—or the "Inferno," as Robert disrespectfully dubbed it.

In Rome the Brownings were immediately caught up in the brilliant life of the ancient capital. Thackeray, all wit and scintillating pleasantries, was among those they saw frequently that winter, and the actress, Fanny Kemble, and her sister, Adelaide Sartoris, a former singer in whose home the best music in Rome was to be heard. Elizabeth found the social pace too exhausting, but Robert went out a great deal and brought home to her the glitter and sparkle of a deeply cultured and aristocratic society.

For each to live according to his own tempo was an agreement made long ago. Elizabeth was easily contented by her own fireside where real friends sought her out. There were compensations now for Robert's absences which she would not have believed possible five years ago, for they enabled her to discuss spiritualism with other believers, a subject for which he had, to put it mildly, no enthusiasm. In the independence and freedom of their present life there was no less de-

votion, only comradeship in its truest sense: an accept-
ance of each other's differences with humor and understanding. Browning might spend his late evenings in
the company of others, but he always dined at home.
Reunion at mealtimes was an unbroken custom which
friends were welcome to share and with which nothing was allowed to interfere.

When spring returned, bringing with it malarial dan-
gers from the undrained marshes of Rome, they came
home to the refuge of which they would never tire in
Florence. Elizabeth's income was unexpectedly cut at
this time by the failure of an investment, and as they
had spent money rather lavishly in Rome, they abandoned a plan to go to England and did not even take
their usual summer excursion to the hills.

The deprivation was not too hard. Robert, after his
months of mild dissipation, resumed work on *Men and
Women* eagerly. A new man-servant, Ferdinando, was
courting Wilson successfully and proving an entertain-
ing companion for Penini. Flush, nearing the moment
when he was never to waken, slept his life peacefully
away at Elizabeth's feet. Fireflies lit the terrace of Casa
Guidi during the long twilights and nightingales sang
in palace gardens close by. Elizabeth and Robert made
the most of such gratuitous delights, as poets can and
always will.

The tranquil interim ended, however, when an unusually early winter and bad news from England arrived simultaneously. The Crimean War, a struggle for
control of the Crimean Peninsula, plunged Turkey,
Great Britain, and France into conflict with Russia.

Robert, like most men living away from the mother country, grew intensely patriotic and restless. Elizabeth was anxious lest Henrietta's husband be sent to the battle area, and Arabel was bearing alone the brunt of an aging man's irritability. Edward Barrett had injured his leg and was permanently lamed.

"Robert is frantic about the Crimea," Elizabeth had written her sisters, but Browning was soon more concerned for her than England. Night after night, as her old cough, which had returned, persisted, he sat up brewing hot drinks over the fire. The dark, sleepless hours drew them closer together, when all was said and done, and in Florence winters were mercifully short. March brought warm days and returning health.

Elizabeth picked up again her work on *Aurora Leigh* while Robert added the final touches to his *Men and Women*. A conference with their publishers became essential and plans for a third trip to England were completed. As the hour of departure neared, Elizabeth helped Browning edit his manuscript, responding to the challenge of the moment with the energy she was capable of in emergencies.

"We are up early working, working," she wrote Henrietta. "Penini's lessons I never neglect—then I write— then dinner—then I criticize Robert's mss."

She had a hurried thought for her wardrobe, to which she gave little attention these days unless Browning prodded her.

"Tell me how bonnets are worn in England?" she asked. "Dropping off behind? . . . that tyrant Robert insists on my 'wearing hats like other people.'"

In early June they were off, Robert and Penini in high spirits, Elizabeth with that inevitable tightening of the heart she knew whenever she left Italy and turned her face toward home.

✎§ *Chapter Twenty-Two*

I love thee to the level of everyday's
Most quiet need . . . .
SONNETS FROM THE PORTUGUESE

FAMILY CONFLICT met her as soon as she landed in England. Her brother Alfred married, and for that mutinous and unforgivable act was disinherited. Alfred was the only one of the Barrett sons to risk matrimony during his father's lifetime. His wife was a Barrett cousin and possibly she had an independent income. The two of them were wise enough to announce their engagement from the safe distance of Paris and to marry there. It was for this reason, no doubt, that Elizabeth was able to write an old friend ". . . there have been no *scenes*, I thank God for Arabel's sake."

Even so, Edward Barrett found ways to show his anger. As soon as he heard that the Brownings were in

London, he packed Arabel off to Eastbourne, ostensibly for a change, but the move deceived no one. It was to prevent a meeting between Arabel and Elizabeth. Henrietta, who had intended visiting the Brownings in London, fell ill and could not leave her home.

Yet out of this disappointing summer Elizabeth was able to rescue one memory that she cherished all her life. Tennyson spent two consecutive evenings with her and Robert. And William and Dante Gabriel Rossetti came the last night for a first meeting with the poet laureate. The atmosphere eased at once into one of unforgettable intimacy. They all settled down to enjoy themselves while Tennyson read aloud, warmed and relaxed by their appreciation into admiration of his own poetry. "How beautiful that is—" he would comment occasionally, and then his deep voice would go on, weaving music through the lines of *Maud*. Meanwhile Dante Gabriel, unnoticed in his corner, worked steadily with pencil and paper on a sketch of Tennyson which was to become famous.

Afterward it was Robert's turn to read from his newly published *Men and Women*. He gave no lyric performance. Browning was a dramatist and an actor of no mean ability. No one moved or interrupted while his characters filled the room with their living presence. At three in the morning the friends finally parted. It had been an exhilarating and unheard-of dissipation for Elizabeth.

October found the Brownings installed in Paris for the winter—unhappily installed—in a dark and draughty apartment rented for them through the kindness of a friend whose admiration for its yellow satin furnishings had impaired her good judgment. By the time they had moved into better quarters Elizabeth caught a cold which curtailed her activities for the rest of their stay. For Robert, however, the Paris sojourn proved the right stimulus. With *Men and Women* off the press he was ready for a new challenge.

Leaving Elizabeth at home, entirely absorbed in the final chapters of *Aurora Leigh,* Browning tucked a drawing board under his arm and went off happily to the Louvre to study the old masters and imbibe some of their spirit.

Paris streets that winter rang with the sound of drums and marching feet. The return of Napoleon's troops from the Crimea amused Penini, who screamed himself hoarse in company with every street urchin in the city and composed a poem called "Soldiers Coming and Going" which threw Elizabeth into raptures of maternal pride. She sent it off to the editor of a leading review in London, to forewarn the critics of budding genius!

Happy in her child's development and undisturbed by visitors in Paris, Elizabeth was able to finish *Aurora Leigh,* promised to her publishers for the following spring. But except for the excitement and pleasure of seeing the poem through the press, the return to England brought only hurt. Arabel was again sent out of town, this time to Ventnor, on the Isle of Wight, and hard upon this blow came the news that their loved friend, John Kenyon, was in the grip of an agonizing illness.

There was little to hold them long in London. Autumn came, blanketing the skies with rain and making them realize that it was a year and a half since they had seen Italy. The interval had been too long. Even Robert could hardly wait to reach Florence and the sun-drenched peace of Casa Guidi.

During the next winter Elizabeth attained her greatest prominence as a poet. In these months also, she touched the peak of her well-being. John Kenyon's death occurred in December, but it was softened by relief that his sufferings were over. Meantime, *Aurora Leigh* was being given a sensational reception.

Public curiosity was stronger than Victorian prudery. Elizabeth had expected scandalized objections to her inclusion of a prostitute in her story—to her championing of fairer treatment for unfortunate women. But those who raised a hue and cry only advertised the poem. In one fortnight *Aurora Leigh* outstripped all the popular fiction of the day by going into a second printing. Three months later a third edition was necessary. Her poem had become the most talked-of book of the season.

On the surge of this achievement Elizabeth was lifted into physical and mental buoyancy. When, in February, Florence staged its annual riot of fun—the Mardi Gras Carnival—she caught the infection for the first time. Browning had engaged a box at the opera for the masked ball—the climax of the festivities. Elizabeth had not expected to go, but at the last minute the weather turned mild and her spirits soared. The

Brownings' man, Ferdinando, rushed out to hire her a domino, and in half an hour she was off with Robert in a cab through the laughing, jostling crowds.

At the ball, a monstrous affair to which all Florence went, the Brownings caught sight of their own staid Wilson, behaving with an abandon unknown in England. Elizabeth herself was tapped on the shoulder by more than one masked gallant. It was two in the morning before she left Robert and their guests and slipped quietly home, satisfied that for once in her life she had touched the borders of sheer, wanton gayety.

And then, as so often for her, the high tide of contentment receded abruptly. News came from England that Edward Barrett had died suddenly. He could hardly inflict as much anguish in going as he had in his strangely warped living. His passing closed a bitter chapter in family life. Elizabeth seemed to accept the tidings with more fortitude than Browning had feared possible, but she hid from him a tendency to brood.

"Occupation is the only thing to keep one on one's feet a little—that I know well," she wrote Henrietta. "I take up books—but my heart goes walking up and down through that house of Wimpole Street, till it is tired, tired."

Elizabeth never again returned to England. No business made the trip necessary. After the publication of *Men and Women* and *Aurora Leigh* there followed a fallow period, especially for Robert, out of which no major poetic work emerged. With the income from two legacies, left each of them by John Kenyon, the Brownings were now altogether free from financial worries. For Browning, life became perhaps too unhurried and easy. He allowed his work for a time to depend on his mood, while he drifted into leisurely pursuits that were harmless and congenial and not very conducive to writing. In Elizabeth's letters at this time may be detected a mild disappointment, too affectionately and tolerantly felt to be called censure.

After a brief summer excursion into France to join Browning's father and sister, the winter of 1859 hastened them south again, this time to Rome. The change, following their prolonged stay in Florence, was very much to Robert's taste.

"He is plunged into gayeties of all sorts, caught from one hand to another like a ball, has gone out every night for a fortnight together and sometimes two or three times deep in one night's engagements," Elizabeth described his life with tolerant amusement to Isa Blagden, adding with a shade of irony, "so plenty of distractions, and no *Men and Women*. Men and women from without instead!"

Younger than herself by six years, Robert had always been older in worldly contacts and experience. Now, Elizabeth found a few wifely admonitions necessary, especially when Browning was commanded to present himself before the young Prince Edward of Wales, then a visitor in Rome.

"Be sure you make him understand the political situation here," she urged, anxious for England's support of Italy's independence, "and above all," tucking an impeccably laundered handkerchief into the pocket of his dress clothes, "attempt no compliments, Robert— you have a way of giving them such an unexpected turn."

Browning shot her a quizzical glance above his struggle with a recalcitrant collar.

"I heard you with my own ears say to Mrs. Story the other day—'I had a delightful evening at your house. *I never spoke to you once.*' "

"Did I really?"

"And—" her fingers busy with his tie, Elizabeth's mouth twitched with her effort to be stern—"that poor artist who lamented that he was never satisfied with his work. You comforted him with—'But my dear fellow, if you were satisfied, you would be *so easily* satisfied!' "

"Well—well—" ejaculated Robert.

He took her in his arms then, laughing his great hearty laugh, and went off to his meeting with royalty, wearing, as befitted Robert Browning, an air of casual but unmistakable distinction, his cane on his arm, his lemon-colored gloves in one hand, his top hat set ever so slightly at an angle.

Elizabeth went to bed. She had, to while away the hours until his return, an excellent book and the certainty of his success and jubilant homecoming.

✑ Chapter Twenty-Three

I love thee to the depth and breadth and
height
My soul can reach . . . .
SONNETS FROM THE PORTUGUESE

B Y T H E T I M E the Brownings left Rome for Casa
Guidi, in the spring, Italian affairs had received a
new impetus through the sudden decision of Louis Napoleon to intervene against Austria. The streets of
Florence were swarming with French troops and Elizabeth was triumphant. Robert had never shared her enthusiasm for the French emperor. It was pleasant to
see her belief in him vindicated.

Through the intense heat of most of that summer
the Brownings stayed on in Florence to receive the
latest war bulletins. Then, with a suddenness as mys-
tifying as it was abrupt, an armistice was declared at
Villafranca, and out of that pause in hostilities was

born an inglorious peace. Louis Napoleon was given Savoy and Nice in return for the withdrawal of his troops, and the Italian people were left stunned and betrayed—their movement for liberation once more in ruins.

Under the shock of disillusion, Elizabeth's health collapsed. It is hardly possible to overestimate to what degree Elizabeth Browning had become involved emotionally with the cause of oppressed peoples. Slavery was too shamefully woven through her family record for her to watch any struggle for independence unmoved. She had once dared to rebuke John Ruskin for his apathy in regard to Negro slavery.

"I belong to a family of West Indian slaveholders, and if I believed in curses, I should be afraid. I can at least thank God that I am not an American. How you look serenely on slavery, I cannot understand, and I distrust your power to explain."

She had thought freedom all but gained for the nation where she had found release from a slavery of her own. Time and again Italian hopes had risen only to be crushed by treason in some form. Severe attacks of illness had always followed emotional crises in Elizabeth's life. Now there ensued for Browning days and nights of anxiety as together they fought off the most prolonged siege of lung trouble she had experienced since her marriage.

Subsequent events convinced Elizabeth that Louis Napoleon's hand had been forced by the combined pressure of England as well as Austria. From then on Elizabeth openly condemned her country's foreign pol-

icy, designed, as she saw it, to further imperial interests at the expense of weaker nations. As soon as his
wife was able to travel, Browning took his family to
the more bracing climate of Siena where he realized
with relief that she would also be removed from the
political turmoil of the Florentine city.

In Siena she put returning strength to immediate
use in a poem called "A Tale of Villa Franca," an
ironic comment on the recently negotiated peace
which she sent to *The Athenaeum* in London for the
purpose of jolting English opinion out of its complacency. Anticipating a rejection, she begged Mr. Chorley of the editorial staff to "see it put in" even though
The Athenaeum was, she knew, opposed to her views.
" 'Strike but hear me,' " she quoted. "I have been living and dying for Italy lately."

The Athenaeum did publish the poem, criticizing it
sharply at the same time—a right to "strike" which she
had conceded them. From this tilt, which she rather
enjoyed, Elizabeth plunged into another and far more
serious conflict with English opinion. The following
winter in Rome was devoted to the preparation of a
brief volume of verse—*Poems before Congress*—dealing
with political issues in Italy. In her preface to the
book she openly challenged her countrymen to play
a more disinterested part in world affairs. But in this
collection of short poems she unfortunately included
one entitled "A Curse for a Nation," which aroused a
storm of protest in England.

It happened that "A Curse for a Nation" had been
first published in the United States, as a careful read-

ing of the poem would have disclosed. It was an indictment of America and Negro slavery, not of England. But Mr. Chorley of *The Athenaeum* did not read it carefully. Being opposed to the politics in the book, he took immediate offense at this poem's title and jumped to the conclusion that Mrs. Browning was cursing her own country. The review he wrote planted the same mistake in the minds of the public.

It was comparatively easy to endure public censure —especially when one expected it—but now friends and relatives allowed a hint of alienation to creep into their letters and Elizabeth suffered. Browning, who would not tolerate criticism of his wife, insisted that she point out his mistake to Mr. Chorley, which she did, in letters, however, which he failed to make public. The impression he had given remained uncorrected and clouded the winter of 1860.

In a mood of increasing weariness and despondency Elizabeth returned to Florence that spring. Writing to Isa Blagden, whose long residence in Italy made her a very sympathetic friend, Elizabeth confessed that what with preparation of some Italian lyrics for publication and Penini's lessons, her hands were too full. "They are soon tired, my Isa, nowadays. When the sun goes down, I am down." She was ill-prepared now for the next blow which fell from England. Henrietta's life was despaired of. The comfort of her letters ceased and Elizabeth had to bear as best she could the knowledge that her sister was dying.

Another summer in Siena amid lovely transparent Italian scenery failed to bring Elizabeth peace. There was too much solitude for haunting memories of home. When autumn returned they did not pause long in Florence but left quickly for Rome. There Robert studied modeling with his friend William Story, and Penini, now finishing his eleventh year, became more and more his father's companion in outdoor diversions. From now on there is noticeable in Elizabeth's letters a shade of wistfulness as she watched the two beings she loved most grow increasingly independent of her. It was as though she recognized an approaching separation. After Henrietta's death, which occurred at this time, she reverted to an old theme often expressed in the Wimpole Street days.

"I struggle hard to live on," she wrote an old friend. "I wish to live just as long and no longer than to grow in the soul."

Her writing went on, undeterred by recent clashes with English opinion. She had submitted a poem to Thackeray, for his magazine, which she well knew would outrage Victorian readers. Thackeray was embarrassed to have to reject a contribution from so eminent a poet.

"My dear Mrs. Browning," he began conciliatingly, *"has Browning ever had an aching tooth which must come out (I don't say Mrs. Browning, for women are much more courageous)—a tooth which must come out, and which he has kept for months and months away from the dentist? I have had such a tooth a long time . . . and never had the courage to undergo the pull. This tooth is an allegory . . . It's your poem that*

you sent me months ago, and who am I to refuse the poems of Elizabeth Browning and set myself up as a judge over her? . . .

"*In your poem, you know, there is an account of unlawful passion felt by a man for a woman . . . I am sure our readers would make an outcry, and so I have not published this poem.*"

To this artful apology Elizabeth replied with suave irony: "DEAR MR. THACKERAY—*Pray consider the famous 'tooth' (a wise tooth!) as extracted under chloroform, and no pain suffered by anybody . . . never was anyone turned out of a room for indecent behavior in a more gracious and conciliatory manner!*" But she stood him down on her choice of subject. "*I am deeply convinced that the corruption of our society requires not shut doors and windows, but light and air . . . it is precisely because pure and prosperous women choose to ignore vice, that miserable women suffer wrong by it . . .*"

The spring of 1861 advanced, and with it a necessity that filled Elizabeth with dismay. Plans had been made to join Arabel and Sarianna Browning and the elder Robert in France for a few months. Deep within her she hid the conviction that her body could not survive the strain of the coming journey.

". . . there is a duty on me to go to France, that Robert may see his father," she confided to an old friend. "You would pity me if you could see how I dread it . . . Don't tell anyone that I feel so." And so to Sarianna she wrote letters full of cheerful anticipation over the coming meeting, and in front of Robert she pretended her old eagerness for travel and a change of scene.

But Robert was anxious. It would have been strange had he not noticed, that winter in Rome, a gradual fading of the lamp of life. He consulted a physician privately, who advised against the journey north. In spite of Elizabeth's protests, grown vehement because she knew herself the cause of keen disappointment to others, the trip was given up and in late May they returned to Casa Guidi.

There Robert strove to master his fear. Surely if they went to Siena she would regain the ground lost. He watched her closely behind a screen of confidence. He refused to admit to himself that he was alarmed. But he was on guard, as people are when premonition thunders at an inner door.

৺ Chapter Twenty-Four

. . . and, if God choose,
I shall but love thee better after death.

SONNETS FROM THE PORTUGUESE

ELIZABETH WAS GLAD to reach Casa Guidi. The tedious, dusty journey from Rome, undertaken by carriage, had tired her more than she let Robert know. Since their return she had spent her time on a sofa in the long living-room facing the cool green from the terrace. Languor seeped through her like a sluggish tide, flooding mind and body with inertia. She wished she need never move again, nor speak, nor open her eyes.

Through her half-waking thoughts one feeling penetrated—unutterable relief to be home. Not an object here but her eyes rested on tenderly; that gilded mirror with the cupids which was still her special pride, those ancient oak dressers that had been Robert's choice. Faded rugs, chairs and sofas shabby with use, all welcomed her back with the mute affection of old familiar things. She wanted not to leave them again.

Strange—insistent, that sense she had of high adventure finished, ended without regret or any feeling save a vast calm, completion, a drifting into peace. She had been a voyager and was now home. With Robert she had explored intangible regions, looked upon new horizons, pushed beyond familiar frontiers.

As she lay, detached, drifting between consciousness and sleep, memory wandered through the past, linked it to the present, and found a meaning for the whole. She remembered an Elizabeth who even in childhood had sensed the wrong underlying the traditions of her slave-owning ancestors; who had climbed steadily out of her own peculiar enslavement. Poetry had led her to freedom—out of illness, out of the clutch of paternal tyranny, to Robert Browning.

And as Robert's love had once been the answer to her servitude and despair, so the latter years had unfolded to her a larger, more universal love—brotherhood, bringing liberation to all nations and classes of people.

The house was very still. Robert and Penini were out, riding the hill roads of Florence. Remotely, from the kitchen, sounded the occasional faint outburst of Annunziata's cheerful Tuscan dialect, the dim clatter of her pans. Elizabeth's thoughts slipped away from Casa Guidi to Sarianna and the elder Robert Browning in France. What a disappointment for them all not to be able to spend the summer together, yet now the decision was made, how thankful she was to be spared the long, continuous effort to keep up with their energy.

Arabel was disappointed too. She thought of her with the same mixture of compunction and relief. How inevitably members of a family drifted apart! How relentlessly growth separated people! A pang of nostalgia for associations gone out of her life drew tears that shamed her. Would she never outgrow that longing to linger in the past when she possessed a present— a present filled with Robert and Penini and the future of Italy? For Italy's future seemed at last to be shaping itself. The skillful statesmanship of the great patriot Cavour was at last about to bear fruit. Why must she feel so spent, when the ultimate of all she had hoped for was at hand?

Slowly the shadows lengthened outside. The silence spread. Belowstairs all was hushed. Annunziata entered the room softly, saw the late afternoon air stir draperies at the window, thought she detected a tremor of chill in the sleeping form on the sofa, and laid a rug carefully over her mistress.

An hour later Penini brushed his young cheek against hers. "You little Ba." He wakened her gently. "We've come home—it's time for tea."

Robert stood gravely, looking at her from the door.

"You haven't heard the news, I suppose." He crossed the room, his eyes searching hers anxiously. "No—you couldn't of course, it has only just reached Florence."

His hand closed over hers. "It may not mean such a set-back for Italy as some think. Cavour died yesterday."

A few days later, the emotional stress following keen disappointment exacted its toll. Elizabeth struggled with high fever and the bronchial condition into which she relapsed so easily.

"The same old cough—it's a habit now." She smiled wanly at Robert. "I shall be over it by the time we leave for Siena."

Nevertheless Robert shut the door of Casa Guidi to all save their intimate friend, Isa Blagden, and her he cautioned to stay very briefly and not to discuss the recent political events.

During the next few days Elizabeth did not know how often she was out of her head. She slept a great deal and when she woke found languid amusement in relating her fantastic, fever-ridden dreams to Robert. Browning hardly left her side, while he talked confidently of her quick recovery as soon as they should reach Siena. Delirium, he reminded himself, had always been a symptom of her illnesses. That her knees had reverted to their old habit of giving way under her was simply a temporary weakness. He had seen her through many attacks. It was foolish to be alarmed by this one.

Fear pushed him to argue against all danger signals, as if by his very denial he could bar the approach of what he dreaded. To his suppressed misgivings Elizabeth was keenly sensitive. She reiterated constantly that she felt no pain, that the comfort of his presence was a selfish indulgence, that he should not forego his usual recreation with Penini.

Her remonstrances Robert scarcely heard, so necessary had it become to silence the clamor at his heart with her tangible presence; so urgent did it suddenly seem to recapture the early enchantment of their solitudes together. And so, in this period of quiet companionship, and perhaps out of a hidden knowledge that it was to be their last, the fervor which they had known in their hearts' youth came back.

On the night of June 29th, Robert had watched late. Apprehension weighed on him too heavily now to be denied. Her sleep had seemed all day dangerously close to stupor.

Conscious of his great weariness, Elizabeth urged Robert to go to bed. "You're making too much of this —I'm quite comfortable—really better."

But Robert remained at his post. At four in the morning, her hands and feet felt abnormally cold to his touch. He roused Annunziata and sent her for the doctor, over Elizabeth's protest.

"You are determined to make an exaggerated case of it." She laughed weakly, and the slight laugh started a cough.

Robert held her until the paroxysm was over.

"Better now?" he asked, as her head fell against his shoulder.

"Beautiful—" whispered Elizabeth and smiled at him. Then with a quick effort, as though there was no time for what she must do, she raised her face. But her kiss never reached his lips.

Lightly, instantly—like a candle-flame blown out—
she died in his arms.

❧

INSCRIBED on marble, and fastened to the walls of Casa
Guidi, there hangs now Italy's tribute to the woman
who shared the nation's birth-pangs, and who, in a
period of world-wide imperialism, dared raise the issue
of international brotherhood.

HERE WROTE AND DIED

Elizabeth Barrett Browning

WHO IN HER WOMAN'S HEART UNITED

THE LEARNING OF A SCHOLAR WITH THE SPIRIT

OF A POET

AND OUT OF HER VERSES WROUGHT A BAND OF GOLD

'TWIXT ITALY AND ENGLAND

In gratitude this stone is placed
by the city of Florence.
1861

❧ Bibliography

BROWNING, ELIZABETH BARRETT: *Complete Poetical Works,* edited by Harriet Waters Preston. Cambridge edition. Boston: Houghton Mifflin, 1900.

——. *Hitherto Unpublished Poems and Stories,* edited by H. Buxton Forman. 2 vols. The Boston Bibliophile Society, 1914.

——. *The Letters of Elizabeth Barrett Browning,* edited by Frederic G. Kenyon. 2 vols. London: Macmillan, 1897.

——. *Elizabeth Barrett Browning: Letters to her Sister, 1846-1859,* edited by Leonard Huxley. New York: Dutton, 1929.

——. *Letters from Elizabeth Barrett to B. R. Haydon,* edited by Martha Hale Shackford. New York: Oxford, 1939.

——. *Letters of Elizabeth Barrett Browning Addressed to Richard Hengist Horne,* edited by S. R. Townshend Mayer. 2 vols. London: Richard Bentley, 1888.

——. *Twenty-two Unpublished Letters of Elizabeth Barrett Browning and Robert Browning, Addressed to Henrietta and Arabella Moulton-Barrett.* New York: United Feature Syndicate, 1935.

BROWNING, ROBERT: *Complete Poetical Works,* edited by Horace E. Scudder. Cambridge edition. Boston: Houghton Mifflin, 1895.

——. *Letters of Robert and Elizabeth Browning.* 2 vols. New York: Harper, 1898.

BOAZ, LOUISE: *Elizabeth Barrett Browning.* New York: Longman's, Green, 1930.

CHESTERTON, G. K.: *Robert Browning.* New York: Macmillan, 1903.

CLARKE, ISABEL C.: *Elizabeth Barrett Browning: A Portrait.* London: Hutchinson, 1935.

HEWLETT, DOROTHY: *Elizabeth Barrett Browning: A Life.* New York: Knopf, 1952.

MARKS, JEANNETTE: *The Family of the Barrett.* New York: Macmillan, 1938.

McCORMICK, JAMES P.: *As a Flame Springs. The Romance of Robert and Elizabeth Barrett Browning.* New York: Scribner's, 1940.

ORR, MRS. SUTHERLAND: *Life and Letters of Robert Browning.* Boston: Houghton Mifflin, 1908.

RITCHIE, ANNA ISABELLA: "Elizabeth Barrett Browning," *Dictionary of National Biography.* London: Oxford, 1917, 1921.

WINWAR, FRANCES: *The Immortal Lovers.* New York: Harper, 1950.

◅§ *A Note on the Type*

IN WHICH THIS BOOK IS SET

THE TEXT of this book is set in Caledonia, a Linotype face designed by W. A. Dwiggins. This type belongs to the family of printing types called "modern face" by printers—a term used to mark the change in style of type-letters that occurred about 1800. Caledonia borders on the general design of Scotch Modern, but is more freely drawn than that letter.